～BOAT TRIPS IN～ DEVON & CORNWALL

DEVON STAR SHIPPING CO LTD
Cruising Department Telephone 65197 or 7292

Book Now FOR **SHORT SEA CRUISES**

TORBAY PRINCE

★★ **TORBAY PRINCE** ★★

LICENSED TO CARRY 214 PASSENGERS

SAILING DAILY from PRINCESS PIER (near Bandstand)

IAN BOYLE

Published by: Ferry Publications, PO Box 33, Ramsey, Isle of Man IM99 4LP
Tel: +44 (0) 1624 898445 Fax: +44 (0) 1624 898449
E-mail: FerryPubs@manx.net Website: www.ferrypubs.co.uk

First published 2010

Published by: Lily Publications Ltd under the Ferry Publications imprint

Typeset in Bodoni, News Gothic and Zurich

ISBN 978-1-906608-26-2

CONTENTS

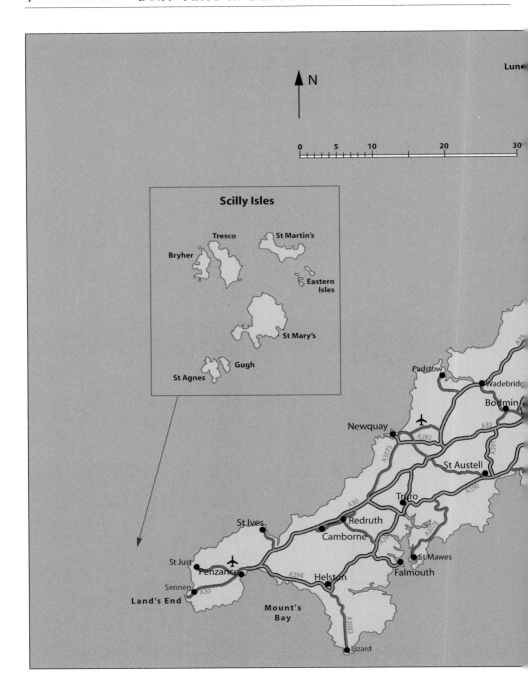

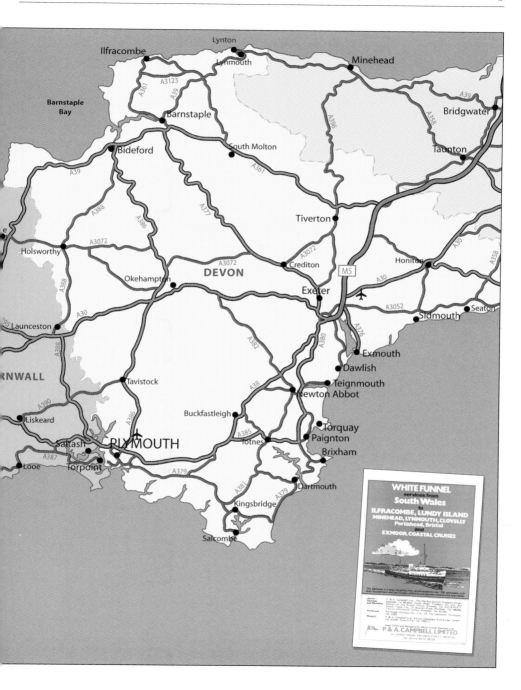

Introduction

The counties of Devon and Cornwall provide some of the most attractive coastal scenery anywhere within the British Isles and a plethora of small boat operators exists to enable visitors to witness and enjoy their wide variety of landscapes from the water. The vessels operated vary from those of the latest fibre-glass construction to pre-war clinker-built boats of noble heritage. Owners take great pride in maintaining their traditional wooden boats and the *Duchess of Cornwall* at Falmouth is a spectacular modern vessel built using traditional methods, and named by the Duchess of Cornwall and Prince Charles in 2008. Some of the historic vessels visited the Dunkirk beaches, whilst *The Fairmile* at Torquay was built as a Rescue Motor Launch in the war.

In addition to the purely excursion boats which operate on a seasonal basis, Devon and Cornwall boast an interesting selection of ferries which are a vital part of the region's infrastructure across the series of deep flooded valleys that dissect its southern coast. If this fascinating array of ferries and excursion boats is not enough, beyond Land's End we come to the Isles of Scilly which rely on their maritime connections as a vital lifeline with the rest of Britain. Here too, small ships are operated from St. Mary's to the other islands and out into the Atlantic to the famous Bishop Rock lighthouse.

Guide to Using this Book

The tables in this book show:

VESSEL NAME	DATE BUILT	GROSS TONS	LENGTH OVERALL	PASSENGERS	COMMENTS
Name	1900	115grt	30.5m	397p	Comments

I wish to thank the following for their assistance with this book: Geoff Hamer, Alan Kittridge, Luke Farley, Andrew Cooke, Rhos Newman, John Pill, Mike Tedstone, Graham Thorne, plus the many boat owners who responded to information requests.

Many small excursion boat operations are affected by weather and tidal conditions and prospective passengers should always confirm sailings with the owners by phone or email before travelling long distances. A phone number is supplied for all operators, and email and website addresses are provided wherever possible. For some operators emailing is only possible through their website.

Whilst every effort has been made to ensure that the facts contained here are correct for Spring 2010, neither the publishers nor the writer can accept any responsibility for errors contained herein. We would, however, appreciate comments from readers if any errors are found.

DEVON

North Devon

The mainstay of passenger services since the 1880s along the north Devon coast was the fleet of paddle steamers and later motor ships of P&A Campbell. These sailings ceased with the sale of the *Balmoral* in 1981, but the preserved *Waverley* of the Paddle Steamer Preservation Society had already visited the Bristol Channel in 1979 on the first of her annual trips away from the Clyde. The service provided by the *Waverley* was briefly augmented in 1981 by the *Prince Ivanhoe*, previously the Isle of Wight ferry *Shanklin*, but her end came after only two months when she hit rocks off the Gower Coast. The ship was safely evacuated, but the vessel was a constructive loss. The *Balmoral* returned in 1986, and has run summer seasons since then in addition to pre-season visits to other coastal areas. Sailings to the island of Lundy from Bideford and Ilfracombe are maintained by the passenger and cargo motor vessel *Oldenburg*, one of the few surviving ships of this type around the coasts of Great Britain.

South Devon

Coastal services along the south eastern coast of Devon were run by the Devon Dock, Pier & Steamship Company of Exmouth. They ran the paddle steamers *Duchess of Devonshire* and *Duke of Devonshire* between the 1880s and 1930s. These were small purpose-designed vessels which could run onto the beach, landing passengers over the bow on a special gangplank arrangement, since piers did not exist at the coastal resorts. The *Duchess of Devonshire* finally came to grief in 1934 whilst engaged in this fairly risky operation, although

Paddle steamer **Duke of Devonshire** (1896-1933) approaching Torquay

she had new owners by that time. Her sister the *Duke of Devonshire* survived much longer, working along the Dorset coast as the *Consul* for Cosens of Weymouth. The Devon Dock company had extensive interests in the area, including Exmouth Docks, piers at Exmouth and Teignmouth, the Exmouth-Starcross ferry and a small steamer running between Torquay and Brixham. Most other services in south Devon were estuarial or local.

River Exe

It is still possible to travel all the way from Exeter to the sea on the Exeter Ship Canal and the River Exe using different boats (special trips occasionally run the whole distance).

The Exmouth-Starcross ferry was one of the many enterprises of the Devon Dock, Pier & Steamship Company who continued to run it until the 1980s. Their vessel *Orcombe* is still in use on the ferry, now run by the Rackley family, who also operate the Dunkirk veteran *My Queen* on river and coastal cruises. Stuart Line also runs an extensive range of sailings from Exmouth with their vessels *Pride of Exmouth* and *Tudor Rose*.

River Teign

Records show that a ferry has run across the River Teign from Teignmouth to Shaldon for a millennium, despite a parallel bridge being built in 1827. There has been a break in this service since October 2009 but the ferry *T&S No.4* (built 1946) is due to be repaired and operational again from May 2010.

King Edward ran on the Torquay-Brixham ferry until the 1930s

Prince (1891-c1923) leaving Starcross for Exmouth

Exonia (1947-1973) leaving Starcross for Exmouth

Tor Bay

Torquay is the largest resort in the West Country and has long been a centre for excursion boats. Few large vessels were based there however, and none was successful. They included the *Pride of Devon* (ex-*Walton Belle*) and P&A Campbell's impressive turbine the *Empress Queen*. In the 1980s, Torbay Seaways successfully ran first the *Devoniun* (ex-*Scillonian* and *Devonia*) and then the ex-MacBraynes *Hebrides* car ferry (also renamed *Devoniun*) on services to the Channel Islands. Sadly, the passenger/car service was withdrawn in 1990 after the company was bought by Huelin Renouf Shipping.

The Devon Dock, Pier & Steamship Company ran the steamers *King Edward* and *Lord Kitchener* (later renamed *Countess of Devon*) on a ferry service between Torquay and Brixham until around 1930. After the war, the Western Lady Ferry service was started using (mainly) ex-Royal Navy Fairmile B motor launches. These were available cheaply (engines removed) and many were bought by excursion operators throughout the UK (and indeed the world, since vessels were sold locally in all theatres of war). At Torquay the boats were all named *Western Lady* with suffix numbers, and the last two ran until 2006 when they were replaced by more modern boats. One was rebuilt as a yacht, but the *Western Lady III* ran briefly from Swanage before returning to Torquay excursions as *The Fairmile* in 2009.

In addition to the Torquay-Brixham ferry, numerous excursion vessels have run trips around the bay, to the River Dart and along the coast.

River Dart

The River Dart was home to a distinctive series of paddle steamers built for the River Dart Steamboat Company, the last of ten 'Castle' steamers being the *Kingswear Castle* of 1924 (although she used the engines of her 1904 predecessor). The *Kingswear Castle* was withdrawn in 1965, the fleet having been replaced by motor launches, but she was acquired by the Paddle Steamer Preservation Society and continues to run on the River Medway in Kent. The River Dart Steamboat Company ceased trading in 1974 and services were taken over by Dart Pleasure Craft who continue to maintain services between Dartmouth and Totnes today, although in 2010 they were renamed the Dartmouth Steam Railway & River Boat Company.

A number of cross river ferries survive on the Dart. The Greenway passenger ferry runs between Dittisham and Greenway House. The Dartmouth Higher Ferry is a cable ferry which forms part of the A379 between Torbay and Plymouth, crossing the river north of the town. A new ferry was delivered in 2009, replacing an unusual paddle-powered predecessor. The original ferry on the route, designed by James Meadows Rendel as were all early UK chain ferries, was the first in the country.

The Dartmouth Steam Railway & River Boat Company run a passenger ferry from Kingswear station pontoon to Dartmouth pontoon in connection with trains and buses. Dartmouth previously had its own 'station' by the pontoon, now a cafe, despite the lack of trains. The Dartmouth & Torbay Railway arrived at Kingswear in 1864 and it leased the ferry rights from this time. From 1869 the ferry used was the paddle steamer *Dolphin*. The railway was operated by South Devon Railway and it became part of the Great Western Railway in 1876, who built the steamer *The Mew* for the service in 1908, replacing the *Dolphin*. She ran on the ferry until 1954, when she was replaced by smaller motor vessels *Adrian Gilbert* and *Humphrey Gilbert*. When the railway was closed by British Rail in 1976, the Dartmouth-Kingswear ferry passed to the local council until

Regency Belle ran excursions from Torquay in the 1950s (W.Moxley)

Torbay Prince ran excursions from Torquay in the 1950s

The Mew ran on the Dartmouth-Kingswear ferry between 1908 and 1954

Paddle steamers **Compton Castle, Kingswear Castle** and **Totnes Castle** at Totnes on the River Dart

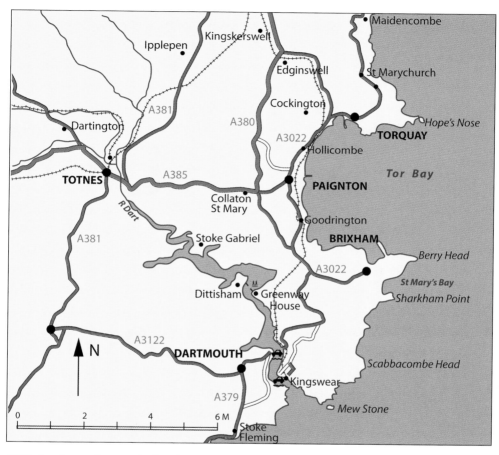

1977 when it was taken over by Dart Pleasure Craft (the Dartmouth Steam Railway & River Boat Company since 2010). One of the current ferries *Edgcumbe Belle* was originally the *Humphrey Gilbert* built for British Railways in 1957.

The final Dart ferry service is the Lower Ferry run by South Hams District council carrying cars on floats propelled by small tugs.

The Dartmouth Steam Railway & River Boat Company is now the main excursion operator on the River Dart, with a large fleet of excursions vessels, including the *Cardiff Castle* built for the original River Dart Steamboat Company. Other excursion companies in Torbay and other surrounding areas also run services into the Dart.

Kingsbridge Estuary

The Kingsbridge Estuary had similar paddle steamer services to those on the Dart, operating between Kingsbridge and Salcombe, but smaller in scale. There were also cargo passenger services to Plymouth. Such steamers were essential to supply islands but unusual on mainland coastal services in the twentieth century.

The Kingsbridge-Salcombe ferry service can be traced back at least to 1860 when a small wooden paddle steamer *Queen* began a regular service. Later vessels, all paddle steamers, included the *Salcombe Castle* (1898), *Ilton Castle* (1906) and *Kenwith Castle* (1914). The GWR branch to Kingsbridge opened in 1893 and having abandoned a plan to extend the line to Salcombe, the GWR began a network of bus services which took away much of the ferry traffic. The GWR bought out the steamers in 1927 to eliminate the competition.

From 1931 various launches plied the route. After the war the *Mermaid*, *Rivermaid I* and *Rivermaid II* ran at various times. Peter Moule took over in 1974 using *Rivermaid I* while the *Lady Elizabeth* (now at Falmouth) arrived from Plymouth for the 1980 season. In 1997 a new 52′ steel vessel, *Rivermaid*, took over. Service and boat were advertised for sale in early 2010 and it is to be hoped that services will resume for the 2010 season.

The remains of the first **Kingswear Castle** (1904-24) remain visible on the River Dart at low water (John Hendy)

Bantham-Cockleridge Ferry (C.M.Dawes)

The Company C.M. Dawes runs a ferry across the River Avon between Bantham and Cockleridge. The ferry forms part of the South West Coast Path, saving nine miles.

Address 6 The Cottages, Bantham, Kingsbridge, TQ73AL
Telephone 01548 561196 - Mobile: 07837 361306
Email -
Website -
Services operated Ferry services run between Easter and 25th September. Daily 1000-1100 and 1500-1600, except Sundays

Burgh Island Sea Tractor

The Company Whilst not a boat, the Burgh Island sea tractor is an interesting vehicle which allows access to Burgh Island at high tide. The 250m separating the island can be crossed on foot at low water. The current sea tractor is the third used on the route since 1930. The vehicle drives across the beach with its wheels underwater on the sandy bottom while its engine, driver and passengers sit on a platform high above. Power from a Fordson tractor engine is relayed to the wheels via hydraulic motors. The tractor is run by the Burgh Island Hotel situated on the island.

The **Burgh Island Sea Tractor** links the island to the mainland at high water (John Hendy)

Telephone 01548 810514
Email -
Website www.burghisland.com
Services operated Sea tractor linking Burgh Island to Bigbury-on-Sea on the mainland at high tide.

Dartmouth Steam Railway & River Boat Company

The Company Dart Pleasure Craft began River Dart boat services in 1972, taking over from the River Dart Steamboat Company which could trace its history back to 1856, but which ceased operations in 1974. Dart Pleasure Craft initially used three ex-Thames boats, all Dunkirk veterans, which were joined by local acquisitions. In 1980, the company acquired the Millbrook Steam Boat and Trading Company (Millbrook Co) at Plymouth, and vessels were regularly transferred between the two areas. They withdrew from Plymouth in 1985 to concentrate on the Dart Services. In 1999, Dart Pleasure Craft was acquired by the Dart Valley Railway Company. In 1999 they purchased the Red Cruisers business of G.H.Riddall, keeping two vessels from their fleet, the combined fleet being marketed as River Link. The company also operates an open-topped bus and a minibuses fleet, and trips combining boat, train and bus are offered. In 2010 the combined rail, river and road companies have merged to form the Dartmouth Steam Railway and River Boat Company.

Address 5 Lower Street, Dartmouth, TQ6 9AJ
Telephone 01803 834488 **Fax** 01803 835248
Website www.dartmouthrailriver.co.uk
Services operated Dart Pleasure Craft offer a wide range of trips, many linking with bus and train rides provided by the company. River Dart Ferry between Dartmouth and Kingswear. April-October: Up river cruises from Dartmouth to Totnes and Greenway Gardens, Dartmouth-Stoke Gabriel trips, Dartmouth-Salcombe trips, Torquay (Haldon Pier)-Dartmouth trips (return by bus and train), plus cruises out to sea to explore the Devon Coast. See website for timetables (tide dependent).

CARDIFF CASTLE	1964	115grt	30.5m	397p	
CHAMPION	-	-	-	-	Dartmouth-Dittisham Ferry
DART EXPLORER	1991	150grt	25.9m	301p	Catamaran
DART VENTURER	1982	94grt	24.4m	320p	
DARTMOUTH CASTLE	1948	81grt	26.5m	297p	
DARTMOUTH PRINCESS	1990	-	18.3m	156p	
DITTISHAM PRINCESS	1995	-	21.3m	181p	
EDGCUMBE BELLE	1957	35grt	17.7m	149p	Dartmouth-Kingswear Ferry
WARRIOR	-	-	-	-	Dartmouth-Dittisham Ferry

CARDIFF CASTLE was built by Bolsons of Poole in 1964 for River Dart services. She moved to Plymouth in 1977 for the Millbrook Co who gave her a new deck housing and wheelhouse. The Millbrook Co was acquired by Dart Pleasure Craft in 1980, and the CARDIFF CASTLE returned to the Dart in 1985.
CHAMPION is used on the Dartmouth-Dittisham ferry.
DART EXPLORER was built by Voyager Yachts, Millbrook, in 1991, taking her original name DEVONAIR BELLE from a local radio station. She was renamed DART EXPLORER in 2001.
DART VENTURER was built as the PLYMOUTH VENTURER by Mashford, Cremyll, in 1982. She was built for service in Plymouth with Plymouth Boat Cruises. Her arrival prompted the withdrawal from Plymouth of

Cardiff Castle on the River Dart (John Hendy)

Dart Venturer on the River Dart (John Hendy)

Dartmouth Castle at Torquay (Ian Boyle)

Dart Pleasure Craft, who had acquired the Millbrook Co. In 2002 she was purchased by Dart Pleasure Craft for Dart service and was renamed DART VENTURER.

DARTMOUTH CASTLE was built in 1948 by Philip & Son, in Dartmouth for the River Dart Steamboat Company. She replaced her earlier paddle steamer namesake and acquired her wheelhouse. DARTMOUTH CASTLE ran on the Dart from 1948 to 1975, and then spent two years in Plymouth before returning to the Dart from 1977 to 1983. Before another spell on the Tamar she was rebuilt with a new deck housing and wheelhouse. She returned to the Dart in 1987 and was a regular performer until 2001. In 2005, DARTMOUTH CASTLE was sold to Michael Barrow and after a complete refit began operating a variety of coastal and estuary cruises from Torquay and Exmouth under the flag of Devon Princess Cruises. She is listed as a Historic Ship (Certificate number: 299) in the National Register of Historic Vessels. In 2010 she was bought by the Dartmouth Steam Railway and River Boat Company.

DARTMOUTH PRINCESS was built as the DEVON BELLE II at Torpoint in 1990 for Bridge of Plymouth. She was bought by Ridalls on the Dart, and renamed DARTMOUTH PRINCESS. The Ridalls fleet passed to Dart Pleasure Craft in 2000.

DITTISHAM PRINCESS was new to Ridalls on the Dart in 1995 and passed to Dart Pleasure craft in 2000.

EDGCUMBE BELLE is a wooden motor vessel built in 1957 at Blackmore, Bideford as the HUMPHREY GILBERT for the Dartmouth-Kingswear ferry, then run by British Railways. Her running mate was the ADRIAN GILBERT, and they ran the ferry until 1976. They were sold by British Railways for use on the St Mawes ferry, but bought back the following year for unsuccessful trials on the Tilbury-Gravesend ferry. The HUMPHREY GILBERT passed to Electro Marine Engineering Co Ltd in 1978, and then to the Millbrook Co in 1979 for the Drake's Island Ferry, where she was renamed EDGCUMBE BELLE. She was transferred back to the Dart in 1985.

WARRIOR is used on the Dartmouth-Dittisham ferry.

Dartmouth Princess on the River Dart (John Hendy)

Dittisham Princess on the River Dart (John Hendy)

Edgcumbe Belle on the River Dart (John Hendy)

Warrior on the River Dart (John Hendy)

Dartmouth-Kingswear Floating Bridge Co
(Dartmouth Higher Ferry)

The Company The Floating Bridge was authorised by Act of Parliament in 1830. It was suspended in 1855 but reinstated the following year with a new ferry. The ferry was steam powered from 1831 to 1835 but then worked by hand or horses until 1867 when a steam engine again powered the ferry. It was closed again in 1874 and reopened in 1876 with a new ferry. The ferry boat named No. 7 was built in 1960 and could carry up to 18 cars. It was unusual in that it was propelled by paddle wheels, although still guided by cables. The current ferry was delivered in 2009 and conventionally uses the cables for propulsion, although it is also provided with four side thrusters to assist when tides or winds are strong.

Address -
Telephone 01803 897542
Email office@dartmouthhigherferry.com
Website www.dartmouthhigherferry.com
Services operated All year services (including Christmas and New Year) between 0650 and 2250 weekdays (0800-2250 Sundays).

HIGHER FERRY	2009	-	250p	32 cars

Dartmouth **Higher Ferry** (Andrew Cooke)

HIGHER FERRY was built for the company in 2009 by the Pendennis Shipyard at Falmouth, on a hull supplied by Ravestein in the Netherlands. Power is provided by two Scania engines (rated at 280kW each), of which only one is required for normal operation.

Dartmouth-Dartmouth Castle Ferry

The Company An on demand passenger ferry runs between Dartmouth and Dartmouth Castle. It is run by three small boats with different owners.

Address 15 Ferndale, Dartmouth, TQ6 3BW
Telephone 01803 835034
Email -
Website –
Services operated On demand ferry service between Easter and the end of October, running from Dartmouth South Embankment (Dartmouth Cottage Hospital) to Dartmouth Castle landing stage.

Exeter City Council
(Butts Ferry – Topsham Ferry)

The Company Exeter City Council operate ferry services on the River Exe and Exeter Ship Canal.
Address River & Canal Manager, Civic Centre, Paris St, Exeter, EX1 1RQ
Telephone 01392 274306
Email -
Website www.exeter.gov.uk

Y Worry on the Dartmouth-Dartmouth Castle ferry (John Hendy)

Services operated Ferry services run between Easter and the end of September. The Butts ferry runs daily from Exeter Quay to the Canal Basin for the Maritime Museum The Topsham ferry runs across the River Exe and is close to Topsham Station on the Exmouth branch. It runs daily except Tuesdays.

Exeter Cruises

The Company Exeter Cruises run services from Exeter Quay to the Double Locks on the River Exe.

Address Flat 3, 18 St David's Hill, Exeter, EX4 3RQ
Telephone 07984 368442
Email info@exetercruises.com
Website www.exetercruises.com
Services operated Hourly service during the summer months (Easter-September) between Exeter Quay and the Double Locks Inn (approx 30 mins sail). Services connect with the WHITE HEATHER to Turf Lock and SEA DREAM II to Topsham

KINGSLEY	1926	13grt	13m	58p

KINGSLEY is a wooden hulled mahogany on oak passenger vessel running a 77 bhp Thornycroft diesel engine. She was previously operated in the Isles of Scilly with the name KINGSLEY and was requisitioned by the Ministry of Transport in 1942 for the War effort. After re-registration at Barnstaple in 1948 she was transferred to Falmouth in 1950 where she operated under the name of EVELINA. She adopted the name LADY EDWINA GROSVENOR in 1982 and was based in Chester where she ran cruises on the River Dee. In 2007, she reverted to her original name KINGSLEY and she now operates as a passenger vessel on the River Exe and the Exeter Ship Canal.

S & M Garrett
(River Exe)

The Company Steve & Marianne Garrett operate the SEA DREAM II between the Turf Hotel and Topsham on the River Exe

Address Flat 3, 18 St David's Hill, Exeter, EX4 3RQ
Telephone 07778 370582
Email seadreamferry@btinternet.com
Website www.topshamtourferry.co.uk
Services operated Up to six daily between April and September between Topsham and the Turf Hotel on the River Exe (30 min round trip). Private charters. Services connect with the WHITE HEATHER between the Turf Hotel and the Double Locks Inn and KINGSLEY to Exeter Quay.

SEA DREAM II	1929	13grt	13m	61p

SEA DREAM II is a classic wooden hulled vessel built in 1929.

Greenway Ferry & Pleasure Cruises
(Torbay/River Dart)

The Company Greenway Ferry & Pleasure Cruises was formed in 2005 to operate the Greenway Ferry between Dittisham and Greenway House, the former home of Agatha Christie. The fleet has since expanded rapidly and now consists of ten vessels, many of which are traditional wooden vessels. Ferry services include Torquay to Brixham, Dartmouth to Greenway and Dittisham to Greenway. An extensive range of cruises is also operated from Torquay, Brixham, Dartmouth and Totnes. A 1940s bus has been acquired to allow circular boat/bus/train tours.

Address 13 The Quay, Brixham, Devon, TQ5 8AW
Telephone 0845 4890418
Email info@greenwayferry.co.uk
Website www.greenwayferry.co.uk
Services operated Most scheduled services run between 1st April and 31st October. THE FAIRMILE runs a full day trip to Dartmouth daily from Torquay (1045) and Brixham (1115), returning around 1730. The Torquay-Brixham ferry runs every 45 minutes (30 minutes each way) between 0945 and 1700. The Dartmouth-Greenway-Dittisham ferry runs frequently each way most days (see website). Return trips run from Totnes to Greenway on days when tides are suitable (see website). The Dittisham-Greenway ferry runs on demand all year (see website for start/finish times). Other cruises run to Slapton Sands, Oddicombe and Babbacombe, plus fishing cruises, bay cruises, wildlife cruises and year round charter cruises.

Bay Belle (Greenway Ferry)

BAY BELLE	1947	-	11m	40p
CHRISTIE BELLE	1982	-	-	100p
CLIPPER	1973	20grt	16.5m	100p
CORAL STAR	1962	13grt	12.8m	63p
DARTMOUTH BELLE	1966	-	10m	40p
DITTISHAM BELLE	1982	-	-	12p
GREENWAY BELLE	1990	-	-	12p
RIVIERA BELLE	1966	45grt	18.3m	80p
THE FAIRMILE	1941	-	-	-
TORQUAY BELLE	1966	-	10.7m	73p

BAY BELLE is a traditional carvel passenger boat built in 1947 by Dixon's of Exmouth. She is the longest running original passenger boat in Torbay which is still in service. Originally called BONNIE BOYS, she has done ferry work, fishing trips and bay cruises in her career. Today she continues in all those roles in addition to working on the River Dart as one of the largest small boats. Acquired by Greenway in 2007.

CHRISTIE BELLE was the DAN II at Pembroke Dock where she was used on liberty work. Arrived in the Greenway fleet in 2008 and was refitted over the winter for passenger service in 2009.

CLIPPER was built in 1973 as the HERM CLIPPER and ran between Guernsey to Herm up to 2007. She joined Greenway from Jamieson, Torquay, in 2009 and was renamed CLIPPER.

CORAL STAR was built in 1962 as the DART'S DELIGHT for use at Brixham. She was renamed CORAL STAR IV in 1976 and ran from Paignton until 1998 before moving to Lymington. Acquired by Sound Cruising of Plymouth in 2000 to work the Mountbatten Ferry. Sold to Greenway Ferry in 2010 and renamed CORAL STAR.

Christie Belle (Greenway Ferry)

Clipper (Greenway Ferry)

Dittisham Belle on the Dittisham-Greenway ferry (John Hendy)

Dart Explorer (John Hendy)

Riviera Belle on the Torquay-Brixham ferry (Ian Boyle)

DARTMOUTH BELLE is a traditional clinker passenger boat built in 1966 in Felixstowe, Suffolk. She was a purpose built passenger carrying vessel formally known as FREDRICK WILLIAM and THE SWAN. When first commissioned she was used for sea angling trips from Yarmouth & Felixstowe as was her sister boat. Later in her life she moved to Allington, was renamed THE SWAN and became famous as a passenger vessel at Allington Lock operating from the Malta Inn, Waterman's Park and Maidstone's town centre. Greenway purchased her in April 2005 when she became the Dartmouth to Greenway Ferry carrying passengers to Agatha Christie's Greenway Garden. She is also used for private charters and for river cruises to the 'Maltsters Arms' in Bow Creek, Tuckenhay and trips to Sharpham Vineyard whilst also available for private hire. The DARTMOUTH BELLE carries 40 passengers licensed by the Maritime Coastguard Agency and has weather cover. Throughout most of her life she seems to have had strong connections with taking passengers to pubs. DARTMOUTH BELLE remains in service providing green transport along the jewel of Devon's crown the River Dart and is licensed all year round. She departs from Greenway Quay and Dartmouth with a free link from Dittisham when boarding her. The DARTMOUTH BELLE is the only passenger vessel currently providing a direct link from Dartmouth to Greenway Gardens, the quickest most direct route.

DITTISHAM BELLE is a local traditional varnished clinker passenger launch which was built in 1982 by Clifford Adams of East Looe, Cornwall. She was a purpose built passenger launch formerly known as SARA used between Looe and Looe Island in Cornwall. Her sister vessel LISA K is still in operation providing a summer service at Looe. Greenway Ferry purchased her in January 2006 and is licensed for day and night use carrying 12 passengers, all year round on the River Dart. She is used as the relief Greenway to Dittisham Ferry and for Greenway Ferry exclusive cruises to Sharpham Vineyard and Stoke Gabriel. She is also available for private hire. She departs from Greenway Quay, Dittisham, Dartmouth and Totnes.

GREENWAY BELLE is a traditional clinker passenger launch, built by J Hinks & Son in Appledore, North Devon in 1990. Previously know as the PUFFIN and then the PATHFINDER, she was used as a hire launch

The Fairmile is an ex-Royal Navy rescue launch from WW2 (Greenway Ferry)

from Dartmouth for some time then was sold and left the river. She returned in 2005 when Greenway Ferry purchased her for use on the Greenway to Dittisham Ferry. Her name was changed to GREENWAY BELLE. She carries 12 people during the summer and reduced numbers in the winter.

RIVIERA BELLE is the only steel vessel in the Greenway fleet. She was originally built by HM Customs at Bideford for patrol around the Falmouth area under the name GUARDWELL. She was sold to Scotland and worked at Ullapool and Loch Lomond for some time before returning to Devon. Greenway Ferry purchased her in 2006 and renamed her RIVIERA BELLE after she underwent an extensive refit. The RIVIERA BELLE now works in Torbay and the River Dart and provideing special day cruises in conjunction with private charters and other special events and has a licensed bar on board. She was reported sold in 2010.

THE FAIRMILE was a Fairmile B Rescue Motor Launch (RML) built by Southampton Steam Joinery Ltd in 1941 and commissioned as RML497 in July 1942. This Fairmile B Motor launch was stationed with 62nd ML Flotillas at Portland between 1942 and 1944. She was then transferred to Kirkwall in January 1944 on anti-submarine target towing duties until August when she sent to Appledore. She joined the 69th Flotilla based at Felixstowe until eventually being sold off at Itchenor in 1947 and entering service with the Western Lady Ferry between Brixham and Torquay in that same year as the WESTERN LADY III. The WESTERN LADY III was recently withdrawn at Torbay, but returned to service from Swanage for Fairmile Classic Cruises in 2007 and 2008 running cruises along the Dorset coast and to Yarmouth (Isle of Wight). Services ran again in 2008. In June 2009 the WESTERN LADY III was bought by the Greenway Ferry and entered service later in the summer of 2009 as THE FAIRMILE between Torbay, Dartmouth and Greenway, after a very substantial refit.

TORQUAY BELLE is a famous passenger boat which was built as HARPOON in Guernsey by C.P. Wilson. She was built after Mr Wilson completed a study on Sea Gulls and wanted to recreate a vessel which was as safe as a Gull on water, hence her unusual styling. The Duke of Edinburgh travelled on her whilst in Guernsey, when her name was TYPHOON. In 1999 TYPHOON moved to Torbay. She joined the Greenway Ferry in 2007 and runs on the service from Brixham to Torquay. She has a licensed bar on board and is licensed throughout Torbay, the River Dart and Exmouth. In 2008 TORQUAY BELLE underwent a full refit.

Ilfracombe Princess
(J Barbeary)

The Company The ILFRACOMBE PRINCESS operates wildlife and coastal cruises from Ilfracombe in north Devon.

Address Pier Gate, The Quay, Ilfracombe, EX34 9EQ
Telephone 01271 879727, 07837 569667
Email mail@ilfracombeprincess.co.uk
Website www.ilfracombeprincess.co.uk
Services operated Regular cruises from Ilfracombe Harbour. Phone or email for times.

ILFRACOMBE PRINCESS	2005	–	14m	100p

ILFRACOMBE PRINCESS is a modern catamaran with spacious open decks and a large cabin.

Torquay Belle on the Torquay-Brixham ferry (Ian Boyle)

Ilfracombe Princess and **Balmoral** at Ilfracombe (Mike Tedstone)

Lundy Company

The Company Lundy is the largest island in the Bristol Channel, lying 12 miles (19 km) off the coast of Devon, England, approximately one third of the distance across the channel between England and Wales. It measures about 3 miles (5 km) by 0.75 miles (1.2 km). There is a resident population of about 30 people. It is managed by the Landmark Trust on behalf of the National Trust. Visitors are carried to Lundy on the OLDENBURG, Lundy's own ship, from Bideford or Ilfracombe.

Address The Quay, Bideford, EX39 2LY
Telephone 01271 863636
Email info@lundyisland.co.uk
Website www.lundyisland.co.uk
Services operated Year round passenger and freight services from Ilfracombe and Bideford to Lundy. See website for timetables.

OLDENBURG	1958	295grt	43.6m	267p

OLDENBURG was built in 1958 for Deutsche Bundesbahn services to the East Frisian island of Wangerooge off the north German coast. She was sold in 1982 to Harle Reederei Warrings for use as a 'butter boat', before purchase by the Lundy Company in 1985. The OLDENBURG has on board a bar, buffet, shop and information centre.

Oldenburg at Ilfracombe (Mike Tedstone)

Kingsbridge-Salcombe Ferry

The Company Services will restart in June 2010.

Address -
Telephone 01548 853607
Email peterj-rivermole@hotmail.com
Website kingsbridgesalcombeferry.co.uk
Services operated until 2009 Kingsbridge-Salcombe sailings ran May-Oct subject to tides, plus other cruises and charters.

RIVERMAID	1997	-	15.8m	103p

RIVERMAID was built in 1997 by Voyager Yachts, Millbrook, for Peter Moule's Kingsbridge-Salcombe services. She is licensed for 103 passengers in a saloon and on an upper deck. The business and vessel were offered for sale in early 2010.

The Exmouth-Starcross ferry **Orcombe** (John Hendy)

Princess Marina on the River Exe (John Hendy)

Paignton Pleasure Cruises
(K.Lane)

The Company Paignton Pleasure Cruises operates excursions from Paignton to Brixham, Torquay and the Dart.

Address 27 Roundham Road, Paignton, TQ4 6DW
Telephone 01803 551744
Email -
Website -
Services operated Summer excursions from Paignton to Brixham and Torquay, cruises to the River Dart (Dartmouth & Totnes), evening cruises to Babbacombe and Brixham. Charters.

DART PRINCESS	2003	-	-	100p
ISLAND PRINCESS	1966	19grt	12.8m	71p
RIVIERA PRINCESS	1947	20grt	153.7m	71p

J & M Rackley
(Exe to Sea Cruises)

The Company Exe to Sea Cruises operate the Exmouth-Starcross ferry, plus local cruises and charters from Dawlish and Exmouth. The Starcross Ferry is one of the oldest recorded ferries in South West England, and was steam operated from the 1880s. It was run by the Devon Dock, Pier and Steamship Co from 1898 to 1983, and they built the current ORCOMBE in 1954. The Rackley family took over the ferry in 1987, and added cruise boats PRINCESS MARINA and MY QUEEN in 2000 and 2002.

Address 6 Dunning Walk, Teignmouth, TQ14 9LW
Telephone 01626 774770
Email info@exe2sea.co.uk
Website www.exe2sea.co.uk
Services operated The Exmouth-Starcross ferry runs hourly from 1040 to 1440 from Exmouth between April and October and takes 15-20 minutes. Later ferries run during the peak summer. Regular excursion cruises include 30 minute trips around Dawlish Bay, a sea life cruise along the coastline towards Torbay, cruises on the River Exe and mackerel fishing. River wildlife, river pub trips, and a World Heritage Coast Cruise are also available.

MY QUEEN	1929	37grt	18m	127p
ORCOMBE	1954	-	14.3m	100p
PRINCESS MARINA	1936	-	15.8m	60p

MY QUEEN is a classic wooden hulled vessel built in 1929 for service between Poole and Swanage and then as MY QUEEN at Southend in Essex. She is one of the surviving Dunkirk Little Ships. Between 1962 and 1970 she served with George Wheeler Launches on the Thames, and later in Torquay and Plymouth. In 1971 she passed to W.Jackson, also on the Thames. MY QUEEN was bought by Dart Pleasure Craft in 1975, and was given a covered cabin in 1982. She was used to take President Mitterand of France on a tour of Dartmouth

Harbour in 1984, the 40th Anniversary of D-Day. In 1987 she was in service with G.H.Riddalls & Sons, remaining with them until 2000. MY QUEEN re-entered service with the Rackley family in 2002, which operate her on local excursions at Exmouth.

ORCOMBE was built for the Devon Dock, Pier & SS Co in 1954 for use on the Exmouth-Starcross ferry, which then ran all year round. The ferry passed to A.Stuart in 1983, along with the ORCOMBE. In 1987, both were sold to the Rackley family who continue to operate it, along with the ORCOMBE.

PRINCESS MARINA is a classic wooden hulled vessel built as the SEA HORSE II in 1936. She operated from St Mary's in Scilly until 1969 when she passed to the St Mawes Ferry Co on the River Fal, where she was renamed PRINCESS MARINA. She joined the Rackley fleet in 2000.

Riviera Cruises
(Karen Hook)

The Company Riviera Cruises operates excursions from Teignmouth to Brixham and up the River Teign to Coombe Cellars.

Address 8 Ivy Lane, Teignmouth, TQ14 8BT
Telephone 01626 774868
Email info@rivieracruises.co.uk
Website www.rivieracruises.co.uk

The **Dartmouth Lower Ferry** (John Hendy)

Services operated excursions from Teignmouth to Brixham and up the River Teign to Coombe Cellars. Charter & fishing trips.

RESTLESS	1964	–	14.3m	70p

RESTLESS was built in 1964.

Salcombe Ferry

The Company The Salcombe Ferry runs from Salcombe to East Portlemouth.

Address 6 Roundbury Drive, Salcombe, TQ8 8LY
Telephone 01548 842061
Email -
Website -
Services operated Salcombe to East Portlemouth, all year.

Severn Link

The Company Severn Link plan to operate two ex-Wightlink Portsmouth-Ryde fast passenger ferries (no cars) on services from Ilfracombe to Swansea (and maybe Penarth).

Address -
Telephone -
Email via website
Website www.severnlink.com
Services operated Cross Severn services from Ilfracombe to Swansea, plus possible links to Cardiff, Penarth and Minehead. Start delayed until 2011.

RAPPAREE	1996	478grt	40m	361p
RHOSSILI	1996	482grt	40m	361p

FASTCAT RYDE was built by Kvaerner Fjellstrand Flyingcat in Singapore as the WATER JET 1 for Waterjet Netherlands Antilles for operation in the Philippines. Renamed SUPERCAT 7 in 1999. Sold to Wightlink in 2000 and renamed FASTCAT RYDE. She was renamed RAPPAREE by Severn Link in 2010.

FASTCAT SHANKLIN was built by Kvaerner Fjellstrand Flyingcat in Singapore as the WATER JET 2 for Waterjet Netherlands Antilles for operation in the Philippines. Renamed SUPERCAT 8 in 1999. Sold to Wightlink in 2000 and renamed FASTCAT RYDE. She was renamed RHOSSILI by Severn Link in 2010.

South Hams District Council
Dartmouth Lower Ferry

The Company There are records on the Dartmouth-Kingswear Ferry dating back to 1365. The current ferry is operated by the local council using two unpowered floats, which are propelled by tugs.

Address Lower Ferry Office, The Square, Kingswear, Dartmouth, TQ6 0AA
Telephone 01803 861234
Email
Website www.southhams.gov.uk/sp-dartmouthlowerferry.htm
Services operated The Lower Ferry operates between 07:00 and 22:55 Mon-Fri, and from 8:10 on Sundays. It runs all year apart from Christmas Day, with limited hours on Boxing day and New Year's Day.

THE TOM AVIS	1994	-	33.5m	85p		unpowered float
THE TOM CASEY	1989	-	33.5m	85p		unpowered float
HAULEY IV	-	-	-	-		tug
HAULEY V	-	-	-	-		tug
HAULEY VI	-	-	-	-		tug

South Sands-Salcombe Ferry (TJ Tucker)

The Company The South Sands ferry runs from Whitestrand pontoon at Salcombe throughout the summer to South Sands beach using the launch HARVEST REAPER. Passengers transfer to a 'sea tractor' at South Sands to run up the beach.

The South Sands Ferry has run for over sixty years, originally using small 12 passenger launches. Gilbert Putt had the current boat commissioned in 1984, using a WW2 amphibious DUKW as a mobile landing stage.

Harvest Reaper on the South Sands Ferry at Salcombe (John Hendy)

The DUKW was soon exchanged for a modified army truck, the DUKW entering a military museum. The Tucker family bought the business in 1986, and have run it ever since.

Address Higher Soar Farm, Malborough, Kingsbridge, TQ7 3DS
Telephone 01548 561035
Email via website
Website www.southsandsferry.co.uk
Services operated Salcombe (Whitestrand Pontoon)-South Sands from April until the end of October. Half hourly from Salcombe from 0945 to 1715.

HARVEST REAPER	1982	-	8.2m	30p

Stuart Line Cruises (River Exe)

The Company Tony Stuart began operating excursion vessels from Exmouth in 1969. His son Ian Stuart now runs the company with his wife Philippa, and they carry over 200,000 passengers each year.

Address 5 Camperdown Terrace, Exmouth, EX8 1EJ
Telephone 01395 222144 (summer), 01395 279693 (winter)
0Email info@stuartlinecruises.co.uk
Website www.stuartlinecruises.co.uk
Services operated Cruises on the River Exe (all year). Guided bird watching cruises (all year – see website). Spring/Summer: Jurassic Coast cruises, day trips to Torquay, Brixham and Exeter. Charters. Speed boat trips on a RIB are also offered.

PRIDE OF EXMOUTH	2003	50grt	19.5m	250p
TUDOR ROSE	1979	-	17m	125p

PRIDE OF EXMOUTH was completed in July 2003 having taken 18 months to build in Cornwall to the specifications of Stuart Line Cruises' company owner Ian Stuart. She is 19.5m long, has two engines and is licensed for up to 250 people. The top deck offers a full 360-degree view, as it is completely open with a folding canvas roof just in case of rain. Benches are removable to allow an outside disco with dance floor. On the lower deck there is a full bar and a heated lounge area with panoramic windows.
The PRIDE OF EXMOUTH is capable of sea travel and therefore sails regularly to Torquay and Brixham throughout the summer months. She also manages to fit in several trips to Sidmouth along the Jurassic Coastline and many Bird watching trips during the winter.
The vessel loads and unloads passengers by way of a detachable walkway. Passengers with disabilities may board easily as can manual wheelchair users. However, some states of the tide may make it more difficult due to the incline of the walkway so it is always best to ring ahead and check. There are toilets on both levels of the boat. The PRIDE OF EXMOUTH is equipped with over 350 life jackets and has five life rafts on board.

TUDOR ROSE (formerly TUDOR PRINCESS on Milford Haven) was built in 1979 and previously the primary vessel of Stuart Line. She has a large open top deck, centrally heated lounge with dance floor and a fully stocked bar making her ideal for everything from an afternoon cruise to private charter parties. The

Pride of Exmouth on the River Exe (Stuart Line)

TUDOR ROSE and her crew are able to cater for disabled people and up to three wheelchairs on circular cruises. Being completely enclosed on the lower deck makes her ideal for school groups or similar. There is a refreshments bar on the lower deck and two toilets on the stern deck.

Tarka Cruises

The Company Tarka Cruises operate 1 hour trips from Appledore when weather and tides permit.
Address The Sea Chest, 20 Market Street, Appledore, Bideford, EX39 1PW
Telephone 01237 476191
Email -
Website -
Services operated 1 hour cruises on the Torridge and Taw Estuaries from Appledore.

NEPTUNIA II	1955	-	12.8m	46p

Teign Ferry
(Teignmouth-Shaldon)

The Company The Teignmouth to Shaldon Ferry across the Teign Estuary has one of the oldest recorded working histories in England. A ferry has crossed the Teign since the 10th Century. The Earl of Cornwall, who introduced tolls, took control of the ferry from the Saxons in the 11th Century. In 1602, Queen Elizabeth I granted the Cecil family the right to run a ferry across the Teign, and in 1712 the ferry rights passed to Lord

T&S Ferry No4 on the Teignmouth-Shaldon ferry (John Hendy)

Clifford. Early in the 19th Century the present black and white livery was adopted; this pattern emulated that of the Royal Navy's men of war. In 1824 the Teignmouth Bridge Company first leased the ferry for £150 per annum then, later that year, paid Lord Clifford £4000 to obtain the full rights. In 1827 a wooden bridge across the Teign was opened. After several partial collapses, the bridge was totally rebuilt in 1931. The ferry continued to operate downstream of the bridge.

In 1908 the ferry T&S FERRY No2 was launched. She was built at the Cremyll yard in Plymouth for £27.11s.3d. A larger ferry T&S FERRY No4 was built at Bulley's yard in Teignmouth in 1947. In 1948 the ferry was purchased by Devon County Council for £3,000. On 13th October 1998 a new 20-year contract was awarded to Teign Ferry Ltd to continue running the service. The operator terminated the service on 31st October 2009, following disagreements with the local council. In 2010 the council accepted the tender of Greg Allen, the ferry's skipper, to run the ferry for 15 years. The T&S FERRY No4 is being rebuilt at a cost of £40000 in Totnes for a return to service in May 2010. A 12 passenger backup vessel has also been purchased. A new company, Teignmouth Shaldon Ferry Co Ltd, was registered in January 2010.

Address -
Telephone 01626 215609
Email -
Website -
Services operated Due to restart in May 2010. Frequent services daily.

T&S FERRY No4	1946	-	10.1m	35p

Balmoral of 1949 (Ian Boyle)

Paddle steamer **Waverley** of 1947 (Ian Boyle)

Waverley Excursions

The Company Waverley Excursions operate the preserved excursion vessels WAVERLEY and BALMORAL on behalf of the Paddle Steamer Preservation Society. WAVERLEY is owned by a registered charity. The paddle steamer Preservation Society also operates the ex-River Dart paddle steamer KINGSWEAR CASTLE on the River Medway.

Address Waverley Excursions Ltd, 36 Lancefield Quay, Glasgow, G3 8HA
Telephone 0845 130 4647
Email via the website
Website www.waverleyexcursions.co.uk
Services operated WAVERLEY visits Devon during her Bristol Channel visit in June. The BALMORAL visits Devon during her summer Bristol Channel season between July and mid-September. See website for timetables.

BALMORAL	1949	735grt	62.2m	800p	
WAVERLEY	1947	692grt	40m	950p	paddle steamer

BALMORAL was built in Southampton in 1949 and operated with the Southampton Red Funnel Fleet for 20 years. She then moved to the Bristol Channel where she became the last member of P&A Campbell's famous White Funnel Fleet. When they ceased operation in 1980, the BALMORAL moved to Dundee to become a floating restaurant. She remained there, unsuccessful and gradually falling into disrepair, until she was rescued by the friends and supporters of the WAVERLEY.

The BALMORAL returned to service in 1986 and to this day operates her main summer season in the Bristol Channel, offering day excursions to popular coastal resorts, as well as making visits to other ports and piers throughout the UK in spring and autumn.

In winter 2002, the BALMORAL was fitted with new engines. The project was dependent on nearly £150k being raised through the help of the Public Sector & local Councils, Supporter Societies and on-board Fund raising Activities which in turn secured a further £750,000 contribution from the Heritage Lottery Fund. This money has now been used to replace the engines but has also helped carry out additional improvements to enhance passenger comfort. For more detailed information on the BALMORAL, visit the supporters' website at www.pswaverley.org.

WAVERLEY was built on the Clyde in 1947 - to replace the original WAVERLEY that was sunk off Dunkirk in 1940. The WAVERLEY was originally built to sail only on the sheltered waters between Craigendoran and Arrochar in West Scotland, but she now sails right round Britain offering regular trips on the Clyde, the Thames, the South Coast of England and the Bristol Channel with other calls at various ports and piers throughout the UK.

Mounting running costs left the then operators Caledonian-MacBrayne no choice but to withdraw the WAVERLEY from service, with the idea of preserving this unique ship. The Paddle Steamer Preservation Society (PSPS) stepped in and purchased her for the nominal sum of £1. It is a credit to the Society and supporters that the WAVERLEY became more than a museum and now operates a full programme of cruises from late May to October.

Western Lady VI on the Torquay-Brixham ferry (Ian Boyle)

Western Lady VII on the Torquay-Brixham ferry (Ian Boyle)

The year 2003 saw the completion of a major restoration project, which returned the WAVERLEY to her original 1940s condition. This has only been with major grants from the Heritage Lottery Fund totalling over £6m and the PSPS.

Western Lady Ferry Service (Torbay)

The Company The Western Lady Ferry Service began in 1946 with the purchase of ex-Royal Navy Fairmile B rescue motor launches (RMLs) by Ron Edhouse. Unlike most Fairmile B launches, the RMLs had had a sick bay cabin on the upper deck, which could be used for passengers. The first acquisition in 1946 was RML 535 which became the WESTERN LADY. She was followed later in the year by WESTERN LADY II (ex-RML 542). These were followed by WESTERN LADY III (RML 497) in 1947 and WESTERN LADY IV (RML 526) in 1949. The latter two boats continued to operate the service until 2006. The WESTERN LADY V was the ex-Thames excursion boat SOUTHEND BELLE which had also run as BRIGHTLINGSEA BELLE. The company also owned a fifth Fairmile B, RML 511 which was named RIVER LADY (she never received a WESTERN LADY name). Ron Edhouse sold the Western Lady Ferry Service to Torbay Boat Construction, owned by John & Dawn Perrett, in 1963. The Perrett family have owned boatyards in the area since the 1880s. They acquired a further ex-Coastal Forces vessel PRIDE OF THE DART, a smaller HDML (Harbour Defence Motor Launch), which was used for River Dart cruises between 1963 and 1988. In 2003 they bought the TORBAY PRINCESS and TORBAY PRINCESS II from Brixham Belle Cruises, and they joined the two

The ex-Royal Navy **Western Lady** on the Torquay-Brixham ferry in the 1950s (Ian Boyle)

remaining Fairmile B launches, WESTERN LADY III and WESTERN LADY IV. The Fairmiles were withdrawn at the end of 2006, and the TORBAY PRINCESS and TORBAY PRINCESS II were renamed WESTERN LADY VI and WESTERN LADY VII to take over the ferry service.

Address Dolphin Shipyard, Galmpton, Brixham, TQ5 0EH
Telephone 01803 293797
Email dolphinhaven@talk21.com
Website www.westernladyferry.com
Services operated Torquay-Brixham ferry service from May-October. The journey takes 25mins and ferries run from 1000 to 1700. Private charters are also available.

WESTERN LADY VI	1981	50grt	19m	173p
WESTERN LADY VII	1984	46grt	20m	177p

WESTERN LADY VI was built in 1981 as the DEVON PRINCESS II for M.D.Barrow's Devon Princess Cruises at Exmouth. She later passed to Torbay as the TORBAY PRINCESS. In 2003, she joined Peter Scott's Brixham Belle Cruises, and then the Western Lady Ferry Service, running alongside the last two Fairmile B launches. When these were withdrawn at the end of 2006, the TORBAY PRINCESS was renamed WESTERN LADY VI.

WESTERN LADY VII was built in 1984 as the DEVON PRINCESS III for M.D.Barrow's Devon Princess Cruises at Exmouth. In 1999, she joined Peter Scott's Brixham Belle Cruises as the BRIXHAM BELLE II. She was then sold to the Western Lady Ferry Service as the TORBAY PRINCESS II, running alongside the last two Fairmile B launches. When these were withdrawn at the end of 2006, the TORBAY PRINCESS II was renamed WESTERN LADY VII.

PLYMOUTH

Whereas the ferry and excursion fleets in many West Country areas remain as large as they ever were, the fleet of the Three Towns (Plymouth, Devonport and Stonehouse) is much reduced from the thirty-five plus steamers at its peak, to less than half that number of motor vessels now. Most of these steamers were running ferry services from Plymouth to the surrounding towns and villages on the five local rivers, although excursions were also popular. Most current vessels exclusively run excursions, although three ferry services remain, the most significant being the Torpoint Ferry into Cornwall with its three large chain ferries carrying huge numbers of vehicles and foot passengers every day. Passenger ferries also remain on routes to Cremyll and Mount Batten from Plymouth.

There have been two chain ferry routes across the River Tamar, the first opening at Saltash adjacent to Brunel's famous railway bridge in 1833 with *Ferry 1*, designed by James Meadows Rendel, as were all early UK chain ferries. She was withdrawn when it required repairs in 1834 and the ferry returned to oar propelled vessels until 1851 when *Ferry 2* entered service. Seven different ferries ran on the route until it closed in 1961 when the replacement road suspension bridge was opened.

The first Torpoint chain ferry, also designed by James Meadows Rendel, was a wooden vessel which entered service in 1834. She was replaced by a new iron ferry in 1871. A second ferry was acquired in 1878 so that a spare was available during breakdowns and maintenance periods. In 1932 a second parallel chain ferry was installed and a third ferry acquired to maintain a spare. The three ferries were all steam powered and fired by coal. Two new diesel-electric ferries were built in 1960, followed by a third ordered in 1966. A third set of

Paddle steamer **Alexandra** (1888-1928)

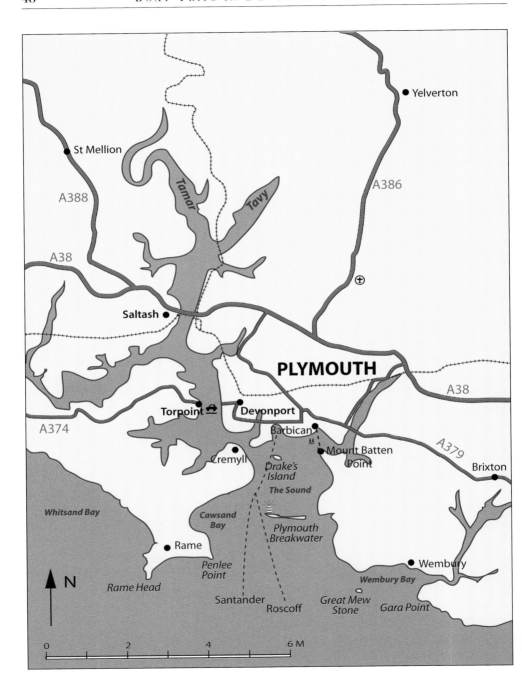

chains was installed in 1972, so that all three ferries could be in service simultaneously. The three floating bridges were lengthened in 1986/87 and replaced by the current vessels in 2004/5.

In the early 1890s, the Saltash, Three Towns and District Company had a virtual monopoly of all passenger services on the Tamar, running a fleet of seven paddle steamers and five screw vessels, plus the chain ferry. However, former director John Parsons started a rival service in 1895 with what became the Millbrook Steamboat Company. To the east of the city, the Oreston & Turnchapel Steamboat Company ran services on the River Plym. All companies also ran excursion trips. Independent of these companies was the Cremyll ferry, owned by the Valletort and then Edgcumbe families. Until 1791 it formed part of the Royal Mail route to Cornwall. The first steamer was the *Dodo* in 1885, followed by the *Armadillo*, *Shuttlecock* and *Carrier*. In 1925/26 a new *Shuttlecock* and *Armadillo* were built, both being steam powered.

The three main companies survived the First World War, but the Saltash company ceased operations in 1927. The Millbrook company became the Millbrook Steamboat & Trading Company in 1929, and also operated buses in the Millbrook area. They began running the Cremyll Ferry during the Second World War, and took over the service and its two ferries fully in 1945. The *Armadillo* and *Shuttlecock* were renamed *Northern Belle* and *Southern Belle* and converted to diesel power. After the war the Millbrook company initially had the majority of the excursion trade. The Oreston and Turnchapel Company lost traffic to better bus services and the company was sold in 1956. Services continued with a successor until 1962.

The Millbrook company was bought by Dart Pleasure Craft (now the Dartmouth Steam Railway & River Boat Company) in 1980. A competitor arrived in 1982 when Plymouth Boat Cruises was set up to run excursions

Paddle steamer **Princess Royal** (1888-1926)

and secured a big share of the market. The result was that in 1985, Dart Pleasure Craft decided to concentrate solely on their River Dart services. They sold some boats to their rival, and the Cremyll Ferry plus *Northern Belle* and *Queen Boadicea II* to a new company, Tamar Cruising and Cremyll Ferry, formed by a former Cremyll skipper. Tamar Cruising have subsequently increased their excursion fleet and continue to operate the *Northern Belle* on the Cremyll Ferry. Her original ferry partner *Southern Belle* now runs from Great Yarmouth in Norfolk. The previous license to run the Cremyll Ferry ended in 2009. After a tender process, Sound Cruising was awarded the licence, but Tamar Cruising have continued to run the service whilst legal issues are resolved.

A new Plymouth operator Sound Cruising started in 2004 and soon acquired Plymouth Boat Cruises. Sound Cruising now also operates the ferry from the Barbican to Mount Batten. A more recent arrival to the excursion scene is Plymouth Boat Trips, running harbour tours with the traditional *Devon Belle* and regular services to Cawsand Beach with the *Weston Maid* that was previously a lifeboat on the liner *Canberra*.

Coastal cruises from Plymouth were mainly offered by the ocean liner tenders run by the Great Western Railway. The main duty of these tenders was ferrying passengers out to transatlantic liners from the GWR's station in the docks. Ocean liner specials were run to and from London, saving passengers considerable time at the beginning or end of a voyage, rather than continuing with the ship to/from Liverpool, London or Southampton. Running excursions was a profitable extra use for the tenders, whereas the occasional positioning of excursion paddle steamers in Plymouth by P&A Campbell, Cosens, etc always ended in failure after a couple of seasons at most. The railway tenders continued providing excursions up until the 1960s, when the liners stopped calling. Latterly these tenders were under the ownership of British Railways.

Armorique (Andrew Cooke)

Brittany Ferries

The Company Brittany Ferries is a French private sector company which has been operating ferry services between Roscoff in Brittany and Plymouth since 1973. Other services from France to Cork and Portsmouth were added and in 1973 a second service from Plymouth was started to Santander in Spain. Their 2010 fleet consists of nine ferries, but only vessels using Plymouth in 2010 are listed.

Address Millbay Docks, Plymouth, Devon PL1 3EW
Telephone 0871 244 0744
Email via www.brittanyferries.com
Website www.brittanyferries.com
Services operated Plymouth services operate to Roscoff in France and Santander in Spain. Outside the West Country, Poole, Portsmouth, Cork, St Malo, Cherbourg and Caen are also served.

ARMORIQUE	2009	29468grt	167.0m	1500p
BRETAGNE	1989	24534grt	151.0m	1926p
PONT-AVEN	2004	41748grt	184.30m	2400p

ARMORIQUE was built by STX Europe, Helsinki, to operate between Plymouth and Roscoff.

BRETAGNE was built by Chantiers de l'Atlantique, St Nazaire, for the Plymouth-Santander, Plymouth-Roscoff.and Roscoff-Cork services. Since 1993 she has mainly operated from Portsmouth, but is scheduled to operate services from Plymouth during the winter 2010/2011.

PONT-AVEN was built by Jos L.Meyer, Papenburg, to operate Plymouth-Santander, Plymouth-Roscoff.and Roscoff-Cork services. In 2010 she also operates from Portsmouth in addition to Plymouth.

Calstock Ferry & Motor Launch Co

The Company The Calstock Ferry & Motor Launch Co was formed in 1998. They operate the summer Tamar Passenger Ferry Service and cruises from Calstock on the River Tamar. Ferries run to Cotehele Quay, unaltered since the last century and home to the barge *Shamrock*. Nearby is a Tudor manor house maintained by the National Trust. The ferry also calls at Ferry Farm (Bere Alston) for those walking the Tamar Valley Discovery Trail.

Address Calstock Ferry & Motor Launch Co, 4 Church Street, Calstock, PL18 9QE
Telephone 01822 833331
Email enquiries@calstockferry.co.uk
Website www.calstockferry.co.uk
Services operated Ferry services from Calstock to Ferry Farm (Bere Alston) and Cotehele (May BH, then late May to early October). Services are tidal and do not operate every day. Trips to Morwelham Quay during June-July and a regular ferry service in August. Other cruises on the Tamar, including Saltash, are run between April and late September. All are tide dependent, so check before travelling.

Devon Bell of Plymouth Boat Trips (Ian Boyle)

Iolaire (Plymouth Boat Trips)

GLORIA	1943	-	11.0m	50p
IDLER	1966	-	-	12p

WJ Gregor
(Newton Ferrers-Noss Mayo/Warren Point Ferries)

The Company WJ Gregor runs passenger ferry services from Newton Ferrers to Noss Mayo and Warren Point.

Address Paradise Cottage, Church Lane, Yealmpton, Plymouth, PL8 2HG
Telephone 01752 880079
Email -
Website -
Services operated Daily services May-September.

Plymouth Boat Trips
(Fish 'N' Trips - Plymouth Hoe Cruises - Cawsand Ferry)

The Company Plymouth Boat Trips offer a variety of excursions, ferry trips and charters under three different subsidiary names. Ben Squire formed the company in 1998 running short fishing trips from Plymouth as Fish 'N' Trips, using various 12 passenger boats. The larger IOLAIRE was bought in 2004, followed by the RONNOCH MOR. In 2005, DEVON BELLE V was bought from Ken Bridge. She was renamed DEVON BELLE and is used on harbour tours under the banner Plymouth Hoe Cruises. In 2010, the Cawsand Ferry will be operated using the WESTON MAID. All three operations are owned by Plymouth Boat Trips Ltd, who have the banner website www.plymouthboattrips.co.uk.

Address 17 Commercial Street, Plymouth, PL4 0LN
Telephone 07971 208381
Email fishntrips@hotmail.co.uk
Websites www.plymouthboattrips.co.uk, www.plymouthhoecruises.co.uk, www.fishntrips.co.uk, www.cawsandferry.co.uk
Services operated One hour harbour tours from Plymouth Hoe using the DEVON BELLE. Charters and fishing trips run by all vessels. Plymouth-Cawsand Ferry from April-September with the WESTON MAID.

DEVON BELLE	1947	21grt	15.5m	100p
IOLAIRE	1982	-	11.0m	28p
RONNOCH MOR	?	-	11m	28p
WESTON MAID	1960	-	14.3m	64p

DEVON BELLE was built in 1947 by Johnson & Jago, Essex, as the SOUTHEND BELLE, owned by the Foreman family. She later ran on the Thames in London and at Falmouth as the WESTMINSTER BELLE, at Poole as the MAID OF WAREHAM and at Exmouth as the MAID OF EXMOUTH. She moved to Plymouth in 2004 as DEVON BELLE V for Ken Bridge. Bought by Ben Squire in 2005 and renamed DEVON BELLE. She operates one hour harbour tours.

Ronnoch Mor (Plymouth Boat Trips)

Weston Maid of Plymouth Boat Trips (Ian Boyle)

IOLAIRE was built by the Elton Boatbuilding Co, Kirkcudbright, as a Staffa to Iona ferry, carrying 50 passengers for the Kirkpatrick family, then sold to Mr. E. Richards from Tenby and used as the Caldy Island ferry. Ben Squire bought the boat in 2004. She is now used for short fishing trips and wildlife trips for 28 passengers.

RONNOCH MOR was built by Freeman Marine, Hampshire, as a Guernsey to Sark ferry for 50 passengers named JOANNA OF SARK. She was then sold to Ross boat trips of Brighton (as ROSSANN) and used for one hour harbour tours. Ben Squire bought her in 2008 and renamed her RONNOCH MOR (the Gaelic for mackerel). She is now used for short fishing trip, wildlife trips and cruises for 28 passengers.

WESTON MAID was built in 1960 as a lifeboat on the P&O liner CANBERRA. She was converted for passenger use in 1980 by Plymouth Boat Cruises for use on the Cawsand Ferry, where she has worked ever since. Ben Squire bought her from Norman Fox in September 2009.

Sound Cruising

The Company Sound Cruising operate summer cruises and charters from Plymouth (Phoenix Wharf) plus the Mountbatten Ferry from the Mayflower Steps (all year). The licence to run the Cremyll Ferry ended in 2009. After a tender process, Sound Cruising was awarded the licence, but Tamar Cruising have continued to run the service whilst legal issues are resolved.

Address PO Box 296, Plymouth, PL9 9WX
Telephone 01752 408590
Email info@soundcruising.com
Website www.soundcruising.com, www.mountbattenferry.net
Services operated Summer dockyard and warships cruises (April-October) from Plymouth Phoenix Wharf, some stopping at Saltash (45mins each way). Excursion on the River Tamar to Calstock (4 hours including 1 hour ashore) or Morwelham (6 hours including 2 hours ashore), dates and times subject to tides – check with the operator. Cruises to the River Yealm (2 hours) or Whitsand Bay (3 hours). Ferry service from Mayflower steps to Mountbatten (all year). Year round charter cruises.

COPPER	-	-	-	12p
CORAL STAR IV	1962	13grt	12.8m	63p
PLYMOUTH BELLE	1960	-	19.8m	120p
PLYMOUTH PRINCESS	1921	47grt	23.5m	147p
SPIRIT OF PLYMOUTH	2004	66grt	18.3m	143p

COPPER is a 12 passenger ex-Thames boat used on the Mountbatten Ferry.

CORAL STAR IV was built in 1962 as the DART'S DELIGHT for use at Brixham. She was renamed CORAL STAR IV in 1976 and ran from Paignton until 1998 before moving to Lymington. Acquired by current owners in 2000 to work the Mountbatten Ferry.

Copper on the Barbican-Mountbatten ferry (Ian Boyle)

Plymouth Belle of Sound Cruising (Andrew Cooke)

Plymouth Princess of Sound Cruising (Andrew Cooke)

Spirit of Plymouth (Sound Cruising)

Northern Belle on the Cremyll ferry (Ian Boyle)

Plymouth Sound of Tamar Cruising (Ian Boyle)

PLYMOUTH BELLE was built locally by Mashford's in 1960 for the Millbrook Steamboat & Trading Company. She passed to Dart Pleasure Craft in 1980 and later transferred to the River Dart. She was brought back to Plymouth in 2002 for Plymouth Boat Cruises and passed to Sound Cruising in 2005.

PLYMOUTH PRINCESS ran at Southend from 1921 to 1958 as the BRITANNIA I and on the Thames as THAMES BRITANNIA up to 1982. She was the first boat run by Plymouth Boat Cruises in 1982 and passed to Sound Cruising in 2005.

SPIRIT OF PLYMOUTH was built new for Sound Cruising in 2004.

Tamar Cruising & Cremyll Ferry

The Company Tamar Cruising began operations in 1985 acquiring the NORTHERN BELLE with the Cremyll Ferry rights. The Cremyll Ferry had been operated by the Earls of Mt Edgcumbe until the death of the fifth Earl. In 1944 the rights were acquired by the Millbrook Steam Boat and Trading Company, along with the ferries ARMADILLO and SHUTTLECOCK which were renamed. ARMADILLO and SHUTTLECOCK were renamed NORTHERN BELLE and SOUTHERN BELLE after WW2. The ferry service was taken over by Tamar Cruising & Cremyll Ferry in 1985, along with the NORTHERN BELLE. The SOUTHERN BELLE remains in use at Great Yarmouth. The licence to run the Cremyll Ferry ended in 2009. After a tender process, Sound Cruising was awarded the licence, but Tamar Cruising have continued to run the service whilst legal issues are resolved.

Address Cremyll Quay, Cremyll, Torpoint, PL10 1HX
Telephone 01752 822105
Email info@tamarcruising.com
Website www.tamarcruising.com
Services operated One-hour docks and harbour cruises from the Mayflower Steps at the Barbican (via Cremyll). All year Cremyll ferry from Admirals Hard, Plymouth to Mt Edgcumbe, Cremyll. Charter trips to the River Yealm, Calstock, Morwelham etc.

NORTHERN BELLE	1926	25grt	20.1m	157p
PLYMOUTH SOUND	1987	49grt	19.8m	190p
TAMAR BELLE	1960	21grt	15.8m	100p

NORTHERN BELLE was built in 1926 as the ARMADILLO for the Earl of Mt Edgcumbe who ran the Cremyll Ferry. She passed to the Millbrook Steam Boat and Trading Co in 1944 on the death of the last Earl. They rebuilt the ARMADILLO and renamed her NORTHERN BELLE. She passed to Tamar Cruising and Cremyll Ferry in 1985, along with the ferry rights.

PLYMOUTH SOUND was built new for Tamar Cruising in 1987.

TAMAR BELLE was built in 1960 as the QUEEN OF HELFORD for service from Falmouth to Helford, moving to the River Dart in the 1970s. She moved to Plymouth in 1994 serving with various owners until

Tamar Belle of Tamar Cruising (Andrew Cooke)

acquired by Tamar Cruising and Cremyll Ferry in 2004, replacing another vessel of the same name now operating as the LOOK AHEAD II on the River Fal.

Torpoint Ferry

The Company The Torpoint Ferry forms a vital link across the Tamar (known at the ferry location as the Hamoaze) between the town of Torpoint in Cornwall, and the city of Plymouth in Devon. The crossing is owned by two local authorities, Cornwall Council and Plymouth City Council, and its operation is governed by the Tamar Bridge and Torpoint Ferry Joint Committee, constituted by elected councillors from the two authorities.

The ferry is operated in conjunction with the Tamar Bridge as a single business unit under powers derived from primary legislation – the Tamar Bridge Acts, and operation, maintenance and improvement of both crossings is funded solely from combined toll income. The three chain ferries provide service 24 hrs a day, 365 days a year and offer a 10 minute frequency at peak times. The Torpoint Ferry crossing is the busiest estuarial vehicular ferry crossing in the United Kingdom, and the three vessels together carry nearly two million vehicles per annum.

There has been a formal ferry service at Torpoint since 1791, operated by vessels using oars, sail and steam. In 1831 the crossing was transformed by the introduction of the first Torpoint chain ferry or 'floating bridge', engineered by James Meadows Rendel. These were powered by steam, as were subsequent vessels until the two

1930s steam powered **Torpoint Ferry**

Lynher II on the Torpoint ferry (Ian Boyle)

Plym II on the Torpoint ferry (Ian Boyle)

Tamar II on the Torpoint ferry (Ian Boyle)

fourth-generation vessels of 1961 (a third was added in 1969). These vessels were substantially rebuilt in 1986, and ran until the current fifth-generation fleet entered service in 2004/5.

Address 2 Ferry Street, Torpoint, PL11 2AX
Telephone 01752 812233
Email enquiries@tamarcrossings.org.uk
Website www.tamarcrossings.org.uk
Services operated Devonport-Torpoint ferry service, 24 hrs a day, 365 days a year.

LYNHER II	2005	748grt	73m	73 cars	chain ferry
PLYM II	2004	748grt	73m	73 cars	chain ferry
TAMAR II	2005	748grt	73m	73 cars	chain ferry

CORNWALL

River Tamar to Mevagissey

Most of the boat operators on the River Tamar were based on the Cornish side of the river, but since they largely provided services to Plymouth and the Three Towns, they are dealt with in the Plymouth chapter. Regular ferries still operate from Plymouth to Torpoint, Cremyll and Cawsand in Cornwall. Excursion vessels based in Plymouth, particularly the ocean liner tenders of the Great Western Railway, would also run trips along the Cornish coast to Looe, Fowey, Mevagissey and Falmouth. The Millbrook Steamboat and Trading Company ran trips to Looe until the 1980s.

A passenger ferry runs between East and West Looe during the summer. Both a passenger and a car ferry operate across the River Fowey from Fowey to Polruan and Bodinnick respectively. A fast passenger ferry service also links Fowey with Mevagissey across St Austell Bay.

River Fal

The River Fal has the largest concentration of excursion boats and ferries in Cornwall. Early steam ferries and excursion boats on the Fal were small tugs, used for both towing and passengers. Subsequent purpose-built vessels retained the tug outline, which resulted in seaworthy vessels which could venture out of the estuary to the open sea and also cope with the sometimes choppy conditions within Falmouth Harbour.

Queen of the Fal (1893-1911) on the Falmouth-Truro service

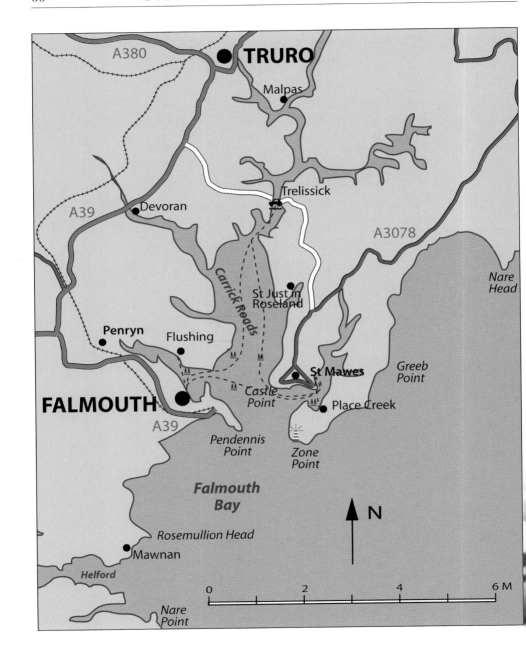

The two main steam ferry services from Falmouth were the upriver route to Truro and across the river to St Mawes. The River Fal Steamship Company was formed in 1906, combining the fleets of the Benney and Thomas families. Both families had started passenger operations with steam tugs. Benney ran the *Resolute* (1877-1902), *New Resolute* (1882-1927) and the first *Queen of the Fal* (1893-1911), which were all single screw vessels. The Thomas-owned *Victor* (1898-1934) was one of the larger passenger tugs in the area and also the last, running excursions until 1933. The Thomas-owned *Victoria* (1900) was a twin screw steamer which permitted a lower draught. She was sold at a profit for service in Mauritius within six months and replaced by a second similar *Victoria* (1901). She in turn was sold for profit to Portuguese operators in 1905, allowing the *Princess Victoria* to be built in 1907, which like her predecessors was twin screw.

The combined River Fal Steamship Company fleet consisted of *New Resolute, Queen of the Fal* and *Princess Victoria*. The smaller *New Resolute* ran harbour trips and short excursions and was sold in 1927 without being replaced. The deep draught single screw *Queen of the Fal* was suitable for sea trips, and the shallow draught twin screw *Princess Victoria* usually ran on the Falmouth-Truro service. *Queen of the Fal* was sold for use as a tug on the Thames in 1911, and was replaced by a second *Queen of the Fal* in 1912. The company ran services until the Second World War when their vessels were requisitioned, never to return to the Fal. The company was subsequently wound up, but their services to Truro are maintained today by the fleet of Enterprise Boats.

The first St Mawes-Falmouth ferry was the steam tug *Wotton* in 1869. Her owners became the St Mawes Steam & Passenger Company in 1872, which ran the ferry until 1968. Later steamers were the *Roseland* (1886),

Victoria (1901-1905) on the Falmouth-Truro service

Roseland (1886-1946) on the Falmouth-St Mawes ferry

St Gerrans (1927-1968) on the Falmouth-St Mawes ferry

Princess Victoria (1907-1942) on the Falmouth-Truro service

Princess May (1894), *Alexandra* (1902) and *St Mawes* (1917). The route is now one of five services operated by Cornwall Ferries. Their other services are the King Harry Ferry across the River Fal, a Park & Ride service from Falmouth to Ponsharden, the St Mawes to Place ferry and Orca Sea Safaris. In 2008 the traditionally built *Duchess of Cornwall* was added to the St Mawes Ferry fleet.

Other passenger ferries run between Falmouth to Flushing and the Newmans Cruises link to Trelissick Gardens and Tolverne. Further local excursions are run by K&S Cruises and members of the Pill family, providing a huge choice of cruising options from the two Falmouth piers on around twenty different vessels.

Penzance and North Cornwall

Penzance is the terminal for the voyage to the Isles of Scilly, which has been served by the long line of purpose built ships of the Isles of Scilly Steamship Company and its predecessors. Local cruises and fishing trips are also available from the port.

The northern Cornwall coast has fewer deep inlets requiring ferries than the south. However, local boat trips are available from St Ives and there are passenger ferry services at Newquay and Padstow.

Duchess of Cornwall on the Falmouth-St Mawes ferry (Ian Boyle)

Cornwall Ferries

The Company Cornwall Ferries operate a number of services in the Falmouth area:-
St Mawes Ferry – Falmouth-St Mawes
Place Ferry – St Mawes-Place
Falmouth Park & Float – Links Falmouth Custom House Quay with a car park at Ponsharden
King Harry Ferry – River Fal chain ferry at Trelissick
Orca Sea Safaris – Wildlife watching cruises using a fast RIB

St Mawes Ferry
(Cornwall Ferries – St Mawes-Falmouth)

The Company The St Mawes Ferry is operated by Cornwall Ferries.
The first steamship on the Falmouth-St Mawes Ferry across the River Fal was the WOTTON in 1869. Her owners formed the St Mawes Steam Tug & Passenger Co Ltd in 1872, and built the ROSELAND in 1886, which worked on the ferry until 1938. She was joined by the PRINCESS MAY in 1894 to be used on excursions. She was replaced by the ALEXANDRA in 1902 and the ST MAWES in 1920. The first motor vessel on the service was the ST GERRANS of 1927. In 1938, the long serving ROSELAND was replaced by the NEW ROSELAND, previously the ROYAL JUBILEE at Bridlington.
After the Second World War, NEW ROSELAND and ST GERRANS were joined by the ST MAWES CASTLE in 1948 and the NEW PRINCESS MAUD in 1950. The company was sold in 1967 and the whole fleet was put up for auction the following year. The NEW PRINCESS MAUD was not sold and remained on the ferry, but the other three vessels were all sold to Thames owners, although ST GERRANS later returned to the Fal working for the Pill family.
The St Mawes Ferry Company Ltd was formed in 1970 to run the ferry. They used vessels NEW PRINCESS MAUD, PRINCESS MARIA, PRINCESS MARINA and NANKERSEY. Ownership changed again in 1978 and 1980, retaining the same company name. In 1991 the company and three of the boats NEW PRINCESS MAUD, PRINCESS MARIA and NANKERSEY were bought by the Pill family who ran the service until 2003, adding additional boats ADRIAN GILBERT, MAY QUEEN and QUEEN OF FALMOUTH.
In 2003, Cornwall Ferries took over the ferry, acquiring ADRIAN GILBERT, MAY QUEEN, NEW PRINCESS MAUD and QUEEN OF FALMOUTH. The NEW PRINCESS MAUD was soon sold back to Pill while the ADRIAN GILBERT was sold to K&S Cruises in 2006. In 2008, the magnificent traditionally built DUCHESS OF CORNWALL was added to the fleet.

Address 2 Ferry Cottages, King Harry Ferry, Feock, Truro, TR3 6QJ
Telephone 01872 861910 (winter) and 01326 313201 (summer)
Email info@cornwallferries.co.uk
Website www.kingharryscornwall.co.uk/frl/ferries
Services operated Two ferry services to St Mawes from Falmouth, one using the Prince of Wales Pier (all year), the other from Custom House Quay (summer only).

DUCHESS OF CORNWALL	2008	-	30.5m	100p	
MAY QUEEN	1939	-	26.0m	100p	
QUEEN OF FALMOUTH	1937	34grt	24.5m	100p	

May Queen on the Falmouth-St Mawes ferry (Ian Boyle)

DUCHESS OF CORNWALL was built by Cockwells Modern & Classic Boat Building in Penryn constructed out of wood using traditional methods and materials and can carry up to 100 passengers. The Duke (Prince Charles) and Duchess of Cornwall visited St Mawes on 11th July 2008 to name the new St Mawes Ferry DUCHESS OF CORNWALL.

MAY QUEEN was built in Aberystwyth in 1939, and came to the Fal from Fleetwood for the Pill family in 1968 for the St Mawes Ferry. She came to Cornwall Ferries in 2003.

QUEEN OF FALMOUTH was built as the MAID OF BUTE in 1937 and served at Rothesay. After service as the MAID OF BUTE she became the MAID OF THE FORTH running on the Forth between 1983-88, and at Southend, before coming to the Fal for the Pill family in 1998 and receiving her current name. She spent one year in Plymouth 2000 with K.J.Bridge and passed to Cornwall Ferries in 2003. She was completely rebuilt in 2004 and is now on the St Mawes Ferry.

Orca Sea Safaris
(Cornwall Ferries)

The Company Orca Sea Safaris operate wildlife watching and coastal boat trips from Falmouth. The company is part of Cornwall Ferries.

Address 2 Ferry Cottages, King Harry Ferry, Feock, Truro, TR3 6QJ
Telephone 01326 214928
Email info@orcaseasafaris.co.uk
Website www.kingharryscornwall.co.uk/frl/orca

Queen of Falmouth on the Falmouth-St Mawes ferry
(John Hendy)

Services operated Regular One-hour and two-hour coastal and bay excursions to view wildlife, including dolphins, minke whales, sharks, seals and many types of seabirds. Book online where trips available are shown by date. Various charter options are also available. Special trips also operated in partnership with the Cornwall Maritime Trust.

SEAQUEST OF FALMOUTH	-	10.6m	-	12p	fast RIB

SEAQUEST OF FALMOUTH is a fast RIB rebuilt in 2009, powered by twin Yamaha diesel engines.

Place Ferry
(Cornwall Ferries - St Mawes-Place)

The Company The Place Ferry runs from St Mawes to Place Creek on the Roseland Peninsular and is operated by Cornwall Ferries. A new vessel was acquired for service in 2010

Address 2 Ferry Cottages, King Harry Ferry, Feock, Truro, TR3 6QJ
Telephone 01872 861910
Email info@cornwallferries.co.uk
Website www.kingharryscornwall.co.uk/frl/ferries
Services operated St Mawes to Place Creek Easter to October (10 mins journey) every 30 mins

NEW VESSEL	2010	-	-	-

NEW VESSEL a new Cygnus 19 ferry was acquired in 2010 for the Place Ferry.

Falmouth Park & Float
(Cornwall Ferries - Ponsharden-Falmouth)

The Company The Falmouth Park & Float service allows visitors to park at Ponsharden, on the outskirts of Falmouth, and take a ferry to Falmouth Custom House Quay, avoiding congestion and improving the environment of Falmouth.

Address 2 Ferry Cottages, King Harry Ferry, Feock, Truro, TR3 6QJ
Telephone 01872 861910 (winter) 01326 319417 (summer)
Email info@cornwallferries.co.uk
Website www.kingharryscornwall.co.uk/frl/ferries
Services operated Ponsharden (Penryn) to Falmouth Custom House Quay. Mon-Fri from 1000 to 1740 (10 mins journey) every 20 mins. At weekends there is a bus connection on the same route.

BLACK SWAN	1942	-	15.2m	75p
KINGSLEY II	1934	-	15.2m	81p

Black Swan on the Falmouth Park & Float service (Ian Boyle)

Kingsley II on the Falmouth Park & Float service (Ian Boyle)

The current **King Harry Ferry** of 2006 (Ian Boyle)

The **King Harry Ferry** in the 1950s

BLACK SWAN ran for John's at Falmouth as the CORONATION BELLE before moving to Scilly in the early 1960s. Here she was in and out of the St Mary's Boatmen's Association over the years but returned to Falmouth in 2003 where she was restored.

KINGSLEY II was built in 1934 and ran for A S Cook at Falmouth as EVELINA II. In the 1970s she passed to Steven Jones who in 1975 exchanged her with the 1924 launch KINGSLEY from Scilly. On arrival in Scilly she became KINGSLEY II, remaining there until 2003. When her replacement MERIDIAN arrived she too returned to Falmouth. Following restoration she has been a mainstay of the Park & Float and has also seen occasional service on the St Mawes Ferry.

King Harry Steam Ferry Co (Cornwall Ferries)

The Company The King Harry Ferry is an iconic part of Cornwall's history. Established in 1888, it connects St Mawes and the Roseland Peninsula with Feock, Truro and Falmouth by avoiding the alternative 27 mile route through Truro and Tresillian.

There has been a ferry at the King Harry Passage for centuries, but there are conflicting stories about the origins of the name. It is possible King Henry VIII visited the area, since he had the castles at St Mawes and Falmouth built. An alternative theory is that it is named after a small chapel which formerly stood on the Philleigh side of the passage, commemorating King Henry VI, murdered in 1471. Early ferries were propelled by oars, but did include vessels capable of carrying livestock and gentlemen's horses.

On 18th April 1888, The King Harry Steam Ferry Company Limited was formed, to acquire the lease and charter for the operation of a steam ferry bridge across the River Fal at King Harry Passage, together with the land and property. The owner of the land was Mr C.Davies-Gilbert of Trelissick, who charged a rent of £24 per annum. This lease was originally for 90 years, but in 1934 it was terminated, and the land, property and charter were acquired by the Company from the Trustees of the Davies-Gilbert family.

There have been seven chain ferries operating on the route. The first four ferries, built in 1888, 1913, 1934 and 1951 were all steam powered. The 1951 ferry was converted to diesel-electric drive in 1956. Further diesel ferries were built in 1962, and 1974, with the current ferry arriving in 2006.

Address 2 Ferry Cottages, King Harry Ferry, Feock, Truro, TR3 6QJ
Telephone 01872 861910 (winter) 01326 319417 (summer)
Email info@cornwallferries.co.uk
Website www.kingharryscornwall.co.uk/frl/ferries
Services operated The King Harry Ferry runs every 20mins from the Feock to St Mawes sides of the River Fal. Summer (April-September) operating hours are 0720-2130 (0900 start Sun). Between October and March the ferry stops at 1930.

KING HARRY FERRY	2006	-	55.2m	34 cars

KING HARRY FERRY was completed at Falmouth in 2006 and is the seventh chain ferry to operate on the route. Like the new Dartmouth Higher Ferry her hull was built in the Netherlands.

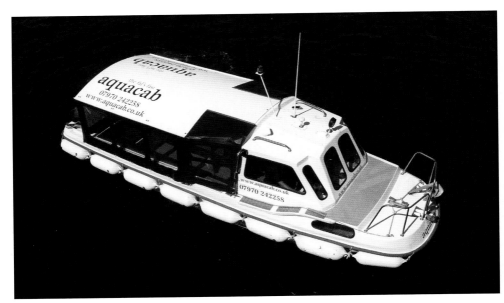

Hi Flyer of Aquacab (Ian Boyle)

Aqua Cab
(Mylor Shuttle — Falmouth-Mylor-St Mawes)

The Company Aqua Cab run the scheduled Mylor Shuttle service between Mylor Yacht Harbour, St Mawes and Falmouth, plus water taxi services in the Falmouth area.

Address -
Telephone 07970 242258
Email -info@aquacab.co.uk
Website www.kingharryscornwall.co.uk/frl/ferries
Services operated Mylor Shuttle from Mylor Yacht Harbour, St Mawes and Falmouth with a high speed vessel

HI FLYER   -   -   -   -

HI FLYER is a Wilson Flyer 24 with a 200hp V6 Yamaha engine. She was acquired by Mylor Boat Hire in 2007 from Wales.

Enterprise Boats
(River Fal)

The Company The River Fal Steamship Company had run between Falmouth and Truro since 1877, but did not resume service after the Second World War. In their place, Harry Johns began running a service on the

Enterprise on Falmouth-Truro service (John Hendy)

Enterprise II on Falmouth-Truro service (Ian Boyle)

same route, using the launches MOYANA and ENTERPRISE. They were joined by the KINGLSEY in 1950. The following year saw the delivery of a new boat QUEEN OF THE FAL built by Frazer of Mevagissey. She later ran at St Ives, the Fal again, Brixham and since 2009 at Belfast. In 1954 the new ENTERPRISE II was delivered from MW Blackmore of Bideford. She was followed by the ENTERPRISE III from the same builders in 1962, and a third boat the ENTERPRISE in 1963, which took the name of the earlier passenger launch. Harry Johns formed the company Fal Pleasure Cruises in 1964 with his son Alisdair. The three Blackmore-built 'Enterprise' boats continued to maintain services until the present day, now marketed as Enterprise Boats. These meticulously maintained vessels run scheduled services between Falmouth and Truro every summer.

Address 66 Trefusis Road, Flushing, Falmouth, TR11 5TY
Telephone 01326 374241
Email info@enterprise-boats.co.uk
Website www.enterprise-boats.co.uk
Services operated Mon-Sat services between Falmouth Prince of Wales Pier, Malpas and Town Quay, Truro from May to October. Times vary depending upon the tides so always check the website or phone the operator before travelling. Due to the tidal range of the upper Fal, some services terminate at Malpas, with a bus connection to Truro.

ENTERPRISE	1963	-	17.4m	130p
ENTERPRISE II	1954	-	18.3m	127p
ENTERPRISE III	1962	-	18.3m	128p

Enterprise III on Falmouth-Truro service (Ian Boyle)

ENTERPRISE was built by MW Blackmore of Bideford in 1963, the third of the three Enterprise Boats in the current fleet.

ENTERPRISE II was built by MW Blackmore of Bideford in 1954, the first of the three Enterprise Boats in the current fleet.

ENTERPRISE III was built by MW Blackmore of Bideford in 1962, the second of the three Enterprise Boats in the current fleet.

Falmouth Pleasure Cruises
(J & F Pill)

The Company Falmouth Pleasure Cruises operate the PRINCESSA on cruises to the Helford River. The Pill family have run passenger boats on the River Fal for many years, and acquired the PRINCESSA to join their fleet in 1986. Since 2001 she has been run by John Pill (as Falmouth Pleasure Cruises). He also operated the ex-Thames catamaran TWINSTAR III until 2007 on cruises to Trelissick Gardens and Smugglers Cottage, marketed as Twinstar Cruises.

Address Prince of Wales Pier, Falmouth, TR11 3DF
Telephone 01326 212939 / 07977 547084
Email fionapill@tiscali.co.uk

Princessa of Falmouth Pleasure Cruises (Ian Boyle)

Princessa of Falmouth Pleasure Cruises with **Haven Rose** (John Hendy)

Website www.boattrips-falmouth.co.uk
Services operated Summer cruises to the Helford River from Prince of Wales Pier. Evening charter trips.

PRINCESSA	1921	-	19.8m	99p

PRINCESSA was built by Camper & Nicholson in Gosport for the Port of Portsmouth Floating Bridge Company in 1921. She was intended for use as an excursion vessel rather than a harbour ferry. The PRINCESSA was used on trips around Portsmouth Harbour and across the Solent to Seaview. She was powered by a two-cylinder steam compound engine by Plenty of Newbury. She was bought by the Solent Boating Company and fitted with a Gardner diesel engine and small deckhouse. The PRINCESSA was employed on Southampton Water and the Beaulieu River until 1986, when she moved to Falmouth to work for GH & WG Pill (later just GH Pill). Since 2001 she has been run by John Pill (as Falmouth Pleasure Cruises), and operates morning and afternoon cruises to the Helford River. She is the largest excursion boat on the River Fal.

Flushing Ferry
(Peter & Janet Hudson)

The Company Peter & Janet Hudson operate the ferry connecting Flushing and Falmouth across the Penryn River. Now a quiet village, Flushing used to be an important local shipping centre and King Charles II granted Sir Peter Killigrew ferry rights between Falmouth and Flushing in 1660. The steam ferry GREYHOUND ran on it between 1888 and 1900, followed by the LILY and EXPRESS. A new motor vessel MIRANDA was acquired in 1914, replaced by the similar MIRANDA II in 1934. She was joined by the NANKERSEY in 1954

Miranda on the Falmouth-Flushing ferry (Ian Boyle)

(which later ran at Fleetwood). In the 1980s ferry ownership passed to F.M.Clynick who had the current MIRANDA built in 1985. Ownership passed to the Hudson family in 2006.

Address 1 Lanhydrock Road, Flushing, Falmouth, TR11 5LB
Telephone 07974 799773
Email mail@flushingferry.co.uk
Website flushingferry.co.uk
Services operated All year service from Flushing Quay to Falmouth Prince of Wales Pier. The service runs a 30 minute frequency seven days a week between 0830 and 2100 in summer, with a break for lunch between 12.45 and 14.00. Evening services do not run in winter.

MIRANDA	1985	-	8.5m	38p	

MIRANDA was built for the Flushing route in 1985, by A.J.Murrey of Falmouth for F.M.Clynick. She passed to the Hudson family in 2006 who continue to run the ferry year round.

Fowey-Polruan & Fowey-Bodinnick Ferries (C.Toms)

The Company C.Toms run a boat yard in Polruan-by-Fowey and operate ferries from Fowey to Polruan and Bodinnick, the latter carrying cars and small commercial vehicles.

Address East Street, Polruan-by-Fowey, Cornwall, PL23 1PB
Telephone 01726 870232
Email postmaster@ctomsandson.ltd.uk
Website www.ctomsandson.ltd.uk
Services operated Daily continuous car ferry service (except Christmas, Boxing & New Year's Day) between Fowey (Caffa Mill Car Park) and Bodinnick. Ferries run every 10-15 minutes. The Polruan-Fowey Passenger Ferry runs a continuous service between Polruan Quay and Fowey Town Quay every day except Christmas Day, running every 10-15 minutes. Passenger ferries also run between Fowey-Bodinnick on Boxing Day and New Year's Day.

GELLAN	2003	-	36m	50p	15 cars
JENNACK	1999	-		50p	15 cars
KALEY	2003	-		48p	
LADY DI	1981		8.2m	36p	
LADY JEAN		-		12p	
TAMSIN		-		12p	

Fowey River & Sea Cruises

The Company Daily summer 45 minute cruises operated from Fowey Town Quay plus charters.

Address Two Longsteps, Fowey, PL23 1BL
Email contact via www.foweycruise.com

Website www.foweycruise.com

Services operated Daily 45 minute harbour cruises (mid-March to early November) from Fowey Town Quay.
Trips to Polperro, Lerryn, Lostwithiel, Mevagissey, etc. The four boats are owner/operated by their skippers.

BEEF'R	-	-	-	24p	
TROY	-	-	-	22p	
BONITA	-	-	-	12p	
GALLANT	-	-	-	12p	steamboat

GALLANT is an Edwardian wooden steam launch, with a boiler and engine built in the 1990s. The other
vessels are modern GRP motor launches.

Helford River Boats

The Company Helford River Boats operate a ferry service on the Helford River.

Address 5 Carlidnack Close, Mawnan Smith, Falmouth, TR11 5LB
Telephone 01326 250770
Email -info@helford-river-boats.co.uk
Website www.helford-river-boats.co.uk
Services operated Daily summer service linking Helford, Helford Passage.

K&S Cruises
(River Fal)

The Company K&S Cruises run excursion trips from Falmouth Prince of Wales Pier, using two very
interesting wooden vessels.

Address Prince of Wales Pier, Falmouth, Cornwall
Telephone 01326 316511 (office) 07811 108918 (mobile)
Email -
Website -
Services operated Daily summer cruises from Falmouth Prince of Wales Pier and St Mawes to the River Fal
and creeks. Trips to Trelissick, Helford River, fishing trips and charters.

LADY ELIZABETH	1924	-	15.2m	90p
PRIDE OF FALMOUTH	1957	35grt	17.7m	127p

LADY ELIZABETH is a wooden motor vessel built by Mashford, Cremyll in 1924. She is named for Lady
Elizabeth Bowes-Lyon (the Queen Mother) who had just married the Duke of York, later George VI. She was
owned initially by the Plymouth Piers, Promenade & Saltash Three Towns Steamship Co Ltd. The LADY
ELIZABETH was their first motor vessel and the last boat to join their fleet. At 50' long she was of shallow
draught to enable her to reach Weir Head, the limit of navigation on the Tamar. She passed to the Millbrook
Steamboat and Trading Co in 1929 or 1930. She originally had twin Atlantic diesel engines and twin screws.
The LADY ELIZABETH was sold to the Ministry of War Transport in 1942 for service in Devonport

Pride of Falmouth of K&S Cruises (Ian Boyle)

Lady Elizabeth of K&S Cruises (John Hendy)

Dockyard and did not return until 1947. In 1949 she received a Parsons engine and was converted to single screw. In the 1960s she received a Gardner 5LW engine, when Millbrook standardised on Gardners. In 1955 she had a brief spell on the Kingswear Ferry, being chartered to British Railways. In 1976 LADY ELIZABETH was briefly chartered to the Plymouth and Oreston Steamboat Co for their Drake's Island Ferry contract. By 1977 she was listed with Mr B Curtin in Plymouth, though this was probably a charter from the Millbrook Steamboat Co. In 1979 she left for the Kingsbridge Estuary running between Kingsbridge and Salcombe until supplanted by the new RIVERMAID in 1997. In 2002 she arrived in Falmouth, where she runs with K & S Cruises. There can be few other vessels, if any, which have run at Plymouth, the River Dart, the Kingsbridge Estuary and Falmouth.

PRIDE OF FALMOUTH was originally the ADRIAN GILBERT. Both she and the HUMPHREY GILBERT were built for British Railways (BR) in 1957 for the Dartmouth-Kingswear ferry service. The service and the two sisters passed into local authority ownership in 1972, when BR closed the Kingswear branch beyond Goodrington. Both boats were sold in 1976 for use on the St Mawes ferry in Cornwall, but were deemed unsuitable (possibly without even being tried) and were bought back by BR for use on the Tilbury-Gravesend ferry. They again proved unsuitable for this route, but were re-engined and offered for sale. The ADRIAN GILBERT was sold to Dart Pleasure Craft, who had taken over the Dart ferry from the local authority on 1st January 1977. In 1985, she was re-joined by her sister HUMPHREY GILBERT, now the EDGCUMBE BELLE. The ADRIAN GILBERT was sold in 1996, joining G.H. & W.G.Pill of Falmouth, proving to be successful on the St Mawes ferry the second time around. The ADRIAN GILBERT passed to K & S Cruises as the PRIDE OF FALMOUTH in 2006.

Mermaid Pleasure Trips
(Adrian Thomas, Penzance)

The Company Mermaid Pleasure cruises operate coastal cruises, fishing trips and charters from Penzance. The skipper Adrian Thomas worked with Trinity House between 1977 and 2004, when he formed Mermaid Pleasure Trips. The company also runs the MISTY BLUE, a high speed RIB.

Address Mermaid Pleasure Trips, The White Shed Ross Bridge, Wharf road, Penzance, TR18 4AH
Telephone 07901 731201
Email contact via website
Website www.cornwallboattrips.co.uk/boat-trips-penzance-cornwall
Services operated Daily two-hour coastal cruises towards St Michael's Mount at 15.00 (plus 13.00 in school holidays). Two, four and eight-hour fishing trips.

MERMAID II	1991	-	10m	35p

MERMAID II is a Cygnus Cyfish, with a speed of 18 knots (10/11 knots cruising).

Mermaid II leaving Penzance (Ian Boyle)

Mevagissey Ferries
(Fowey-Mevagissey)

The Company Daily summer ferry service between Fowey and Mevagissey using the fast launch BESSIE JAMES.

Address Harbour Office, Mevagissey, PL26 6QU
Telephone 07977 203394
Email john@ferry.me.uk
Website www.mevagissey-ferries.co.uk
Services operated Daily summer ferry service between Fowey (Whitehouse Quay) and Mevagissey (Lighthouse Quay) with between three and six sailings each way from 26th April to 1st October 2010. The journey takes 35 minutes each way.

BESSIE JAMES	2006	12.3m	50p

BESSIE JAMES is a Procharter 40 GRP vessel with a Caterpillar 500hp engine giving a top speed of 20 knots (15 knots cruising). She was built in 2006 at Wadebridge, as was her predecessor the HANNIBAL JAMES, formerly the CHRISTINA JANE.

Newmans Cruises
(River Fal)

The Company Newmans Cruises operate boat trips on the River Fal from Falmouth and Smugglers Cottage, Tolverne, calling at Trelissick Gardens.
The Newman family moved to Tolverne on the River Fal in 1934, and ran the launch MYSTERY from 1937. The River Fal Steamship Company had run between Falmouth and Truro since 1877, but did not resume service after the Second World War. In their absence, Rodney 'Pete' Newman began running the launch FREELANCE between Tolverne and Falmouth. She was joined by the ex-Admiralty launches SKYLARK and SKYLARK II. The larger vessel WORCESTER CASTLE, which had run at Aberystwyth, was bought and renamed SKYLARK OF TOLVERNE.

In 1982, Peter Newman bought the HEATHER, followed by the CORNISH BELLE from St Ives in 1996. In 2007 CORNISH BELLE was replaced by the QUEEN OF THE FAL, originally the GAY QUEEN at Rothesay, and the ALICE-MARIE at Poole. She returned to Poole in 2010.
The LOOK AHEAD II returned to the Fal in 2008. She was built in Bideford in 1960 for work on the Fal from St Mawes, and remained there until 1997. Following work at Plymouth and Tewkesbury, she was bought by Newmans and given her original name, where she maintains current services.

Address 3 Riverside Cottage, Tresillian, Truro, Cornwall, TR2 5NG
Telephone 01872 520564
Email newmanscruises@hotmail.com
Website www.newmanscruises.co.uk

Look Ahead II of Newmans Cruises at Falmouth (Ian Boyle)

Services operated Boat trips Mon-Sat between May-September on the River Fal from Falmouth (Custom House Quay) and Smugglers Cottage, Tolverne, calling at Trelissick Gardens. Evening trips and charters also run.

LOOK AHEAD II	1960	-	12.8m	60p
POLGERRAN	1954	-	9.1m	12p

LOOK AHEAD II is from the yard of M.W.Blackmore, Bideford. At 42 ft long and built of wood, she came new to St Mawes in 1960. In 1977 she was running excursions from St Mawes, licensed for 53 passengers and owned by Messrs. Penrose & Davies. By 1989 her operator was the F & B Boat Company, later Balcomb Boat Co. Around 1997 LOOK AHEAD II went to Plymouth where she joined the fleet of Ken Bridge. She passed to Tamar Cruising in 1998, taking the name of TAMAR BELLE, remaining there until 2004. That year she left for Tewkesbury where she ran as the AVON BELLE II for Telstar Cruises. Following the disastrous floods of 2007 she was put up for sale and was bought by the Newman family, returning to the River Fal and with her original name restored.

POLGERRAN was also built by M.W.Blackmore, Bideford, in 1954 for use at Dartmouth. She was bought by Newmans in 2010 after working on fishing trips at Ilfracombe as the GEORGINA..

Newquay-Crantock Ferry
(G Northey)

The Company The company runs a ferry (summer only) across the River Gannel from Newquay to Crantock

Address Fern Pit, Riverside Crescent, Pentire, Newquay, TR7 1PJ
Telephone 01637 873181
Email mail@fernpit.co.uk
Website www.fernpit.co.uk
Services operated Summer only from 22nd May (1000-1600 subject to tides)

WHITE HEATHER	-	-	-	-

Padstow Harbour Commissioners
(Padstow-Rock Ferry)

The Company Padstow Harbour Commissioners operate a daily ferry service from Padstow to Rock, across the River Camel.

Address Padstow Harbour Commissioners, The Harbour Office, Padstow, Cornwall PL28 8AQ
Telephone 01841 532239
Email padstowharbour@btconnect.com
Website www.padstow-harbour.co.uk/phc_ferry.html
Services operated Daily (not Sundays in winter) every 20mins. See website for start/finish times and departure points which can vary depending on tides.

BLACK TOR	1994	-	14.9m	61p
BLACK TOR II	2004	-	16.2m	64p

Black Tor discharging on the beach near Rock. (John Hendy)

Black Tor II at Padstow (John Hendy)

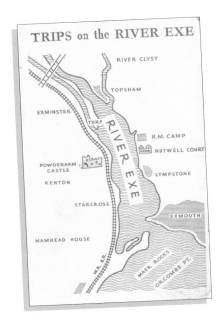

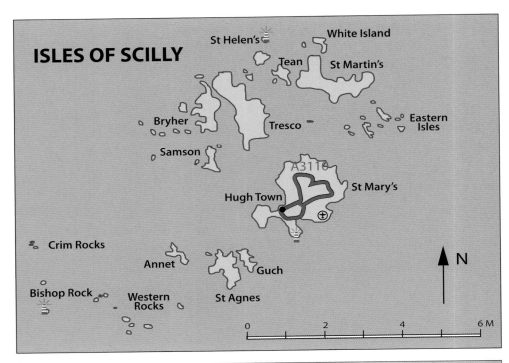

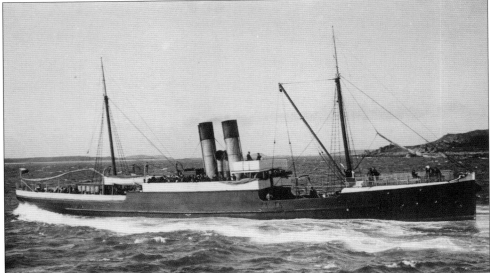

Lyonnesse served the Isles of Scilly between 1889-1918 (Gibsons of Scilly)

ISLES OF SCILLY

The Isles of Scilly are England's only archipelago and are located 28 miles from Land's End. The largest island St Mary's is connected by regular services to the mainland by the Isles of Scilly Steamship Company. Five other inhabited islands St Agnes, Bryher, Tresco, St Martin's and Gugh (which is connected to St Agnes by a sand bar at low water) have regular ferry connections to St Mary's. There are around 200 islands in total and summer trips are offered to many of those which are uninhabited.

Deerhound served the Isles of Scilly between 1905-1907

Queen of the Isles

The second **Scillonian** of 1955 (Gibsons of Scilly)

Peninnis of 1904 (Gibsons of Scilly)

The first **Scillonian** of 1926 (Gibsons of Scilly)

Bryher Boat Services

The Company Bryher Boat Services is a family owned company based on the island of Bryher. Regular ferry services are operated from Bryher and neighbouring Tresco to the other inhabited islands. Summer excursions and charters are available to many other destinations.

Address Bryher Boat Services, Jenford, Bryher, Isles of Scilly, TR23 0PR
Telephone 01720 422886
Email info@bryherboats.co.uk
Website www.bryherboats.co.uk
Services operated All year ferry services between Bryher and Tresco (daily). Ferries run from Bryher and Tresco to St Mary's (M-Sa), St Agnes (SuTuTh), and St Martin's (M). Other trips around the islands, to Bishop Rock Lighthouse and Samson Island, etc. Birds and wildlife trips, plus fishing trips, are also run.

FALDORE II	1981	12grt	11.6m	60p
FIRETHORN OF BRYHER	1991	-	18m	100p

FALDORE II is licensed for 60 passengers and mainly operates charter trips.
FIRETHORN OF BRYHER is the largest boat in the fleet and runs the ferry services. She was built by Chapman & Hewitt at Wadebridge.

Firethorn of Bryher at St Mary's (Ian Boyle)

Isles of Scilly Steamship Co

The Company Between 1858-1872 the Scilly Isles Steam Navigation Company operated the LITTLE WESTERN on services from the mainland to St Mary's. From 1871 until 1918, the main operator to the islands was the West Cornwall Steamship Company of Penzance, who used the EARL OF ARRAN (1871-1872 - 144grt), QUEEN OF THE BAY (1874-1885 - 138grt), and the LADY OF THE ISLES (1875-1905 - 152 grt), the first purpose-designed steamer on the run. She was joined in 1889 by the larger LYONNESSE (1889-1918 - 329grt), which became the mainstay of services for almost thirty years. The LADY OF THE ISLES was sold in 1905, and replaced by the DEERHOUND from Blackpool, although she stayed only two years and was used mainly on excursions. The West Cornwall Steamship Company went into liquidation in 1907, but LYONNESSE was sold to a new company with the same name.

The Isles of Scilly Steamship Company was formed in 1919, and ran the PENINNIS (ex-ARGUS) from 1920 until 1927 when the first of the three ships named SCILLONIAN arrived. SCILLONIAN (1) was followed by SCILLONIAN (2) in 1956, and the SCILLONIAN III, built in Appledore in 1977. Growing traffic had resulted in the building of a second ship, the QUEEN OF THE ISLES in 1965, but she was soon chartered out and then sold for use in the Pacific. A small coaster carrying just six passengers, the GRY MARITHA, was acquired in 1989 for all year cargo and winter passenger services, being laid up in the winter. Discussions are in progress about replacing both current vessels with an all year passenger and cargo ro-ro vessel, plus changes to the mainland terminal location and facilities. A small vessel named LYONNESSE LADY is used to transfer cargo from St Mary's to the other islands.

Lyonnesse Lady at St Mary's (Ian Boyle)

Scillonian III in new 2010 colours (Chris Jones)

The company also offers flights to St Mary's with fixed wing aircraft as Skybus.

Address Isles of Scilly Travel Centre, Quay Street, Penzance, Cornwall, TR18 4BZ
Telephone 0845 710 5555 (International: +44 (0) 1736 334220)
Email sales@islesofscilly-travel.co.uk
Website www.islesofscilly-travel.co.uk
Services operated Seasonal passenger and cargo service by between late March and late October (Penzance-St Mary's – 2hr 40min approx). Occasional excursions. All-year cargo service by GRY MARITHA.

GRY MARITHA	1981	149grt	40.2m	6p
LYONESSE LADY	1991	-	-	12p
SCILLONIAN III	1977	1346grt	67.7m	600p

GRY MARITHA The Isles of Scilly Steamship Company purchased the Norwegian coaster, GRY MARITHA in September 1989, she was named at Kolvereid, Norway in June 1981 after Captain Tor Sevaldsen's daughter. The GRY MARITHA operates an all-year round freight service, proving a lifeline service to the Isles of Scilly catering for the increasing amount of freight required on the Islands. There are three return voyages a week, departing Penzance on a Monday, Wednesday and Friday, stopping overnight at St Mary's and returning the following day.

LYONNESSE LADY is used on inter-islands cargo runs from St Mary's.

Voyager of St Martin's at St Mary's (Graham Thorne)

SCILLONIAN III was built by Appledore Shipbuilders, Devon in 1977 for the Isles of Scilly Steamship Co, running cargo and passengers between Penzance and St Mary's for eight months of the year. She sailed her maiden voyage on 19th May 1977. The SCILLONIAN III has made in excess of 6570 return voyages up until the end of 2009 and will continue to provide the vital connection between the mainland and Isles of Scilly for many years to come.

T A Perkins
(St Martin's)

The Company T A Perkins run ferry services from St Martin's to St Mary's. In addition to the main vessel VOYAGER OF ST MARTIN'S, T A Perkins runs a RIB named LIGHTNING.

Address 2 Higher Town, St Martin's, Isles of Scilly, TR25 0QL
Telephone 01720 422814
Email -
Website -
Services operated Daily services (during the Spring, Summer and Autumn seasons) from St Martin's to St Mary's, with regular trips to Bryher, Tresco and St Martin's. Excursions and charters are run to other uninhabited islands.

VOYAGER OF ST MARTIN'S	1996	-	17.4m	100p

VOYAGER OF ST MARTIN'S was built by C Toms & Son, Polruan.

St Mary's Boatmen's Association

The Company The St Mary's Boatmen's Association was formed in 1958 and currently consists of 10 boats, all individually owned by their skippers.
Original vessels run by the group were the NEMO, KINGLSEY, BUSY BEE, SAPPHIRE, GLORIA, SEAHORSE and LILY OF LAGUNA from independent operators, plus the GONDOLIER and GOLDEN SPRAY belonging to the Isle of Scilly Steamship Company.
The current fleet consists of five traditional wooden boats, one all-weather wooden boat and four modern Kingfisher K50 GRP open boats.

Address J Phillips, Rose Cottage, The Strand, St Mary's, Isles of Scilly, TR21 0PT
Telephone 01720 423999
Email enquiries@scillyboating.co.uk
Website www.scillyboating.co.uk
Services operated Summer services from St Mary's to St Agnes, Bryher, Tresco, and St Martin's. Other trips around the islands, to Bishop Rock lighthouse and Samson Island.

BRITANNIA	1944	-	14.3m	72p
GOLDEN SPRAY	1947	-	13.7m	72p
GUIDING STAR	1933	-	15.2m	72p
KINGFISHER OF ST MARY'S	1995	-	14.9m	80p

Britannia at St Mary's (Ian Boyle)

Golden Spray at St Mary's (Ian Boyle)

Guiding Star at St Mary's (Ian Boyle)

Kingfisher of St Mary's at St Mary's (Ian Boyle)

Lightning at St Mary's (Graham Thorne)

Osprey of St Mary's at St Mary's (Ian Boyle)

MERIDIAN	2003	-	15.2m	100p
OSPREY OF ST MARY'S	2003	-	15.2m	93p
SAPPHIRE	2000	-	15.2m	90p
SEAHORSE	1997	-	17.7m	100p
SEA KING	1947	-	17.4m	85p
SURPRISE	1945	-	14.0m	72p

BRITANNIA was built by the Admiralty in 1944. She is owned by David Badcock, part of one of the founding families of the Boatmen's Association, and has been a member since 1967. She is an open boat of double diagonal construction.

GOLDEN SPRAY is an open passenger launch, built in Margate of mahogany on oak in 1947. She is owned by Roy Duncan, having been bought from the Isles of Scilly Steamship Co in 1968.

GUIDING STAR was built in 1933 by Percy Michell in Porthmellon near Mevagissy, Cornwall. This boat is of Carvel construction and has been in the Badcock family for 42 years. She is owned by Joe Badcock and is the oldest launch currently in operation within St. Mary's Boatmen's Association.

KINGFISHER OF ST MARY'S is a Kingfisher K50 built in 1995

MERIDIAN is a Kingfisher K50 built in 2003

OSPREY OF ST MARY'S is a Kingfisher K50 built in 2003

SAPPHIRE is a Kingfisher K50 built in 2000

SEAHORSE is an all-weather boat with enclosed cabin built by Martin, St Mary's, in 1977

SEA KING was built by Mashford, Millbrook, Cornwall, in 1947

SURPRISE was built by the Admiralty at Christchurch in 1945

St Agnes Boating (D V Peacock)

The Company St Agnes Boating run ferry services from St Agnes to St Mary's.

Address The Barn, St Agnes, Isles of Scilly, TR22 0PL
Telephone 01720 422704
Email john@st-agnes-boating.co.uk

Sapphire at St Mary's (Ian Boyle)

Sea King at St Mary's (Ian Boyle)

Seahorse at St Mary's (Graham Thorne)

Surprise at St Mary's (Ian Boyle)

Website www.st-agnes-boating.co.uk
Services operated Daily services (during the Spring, Summer and Autumn seasons) from St Agnes to St Mary's, with regular trips to Bryher, Tresco and St Martin's. Excursions and charters are run to other islands, Bishop Rock Lighthouse and for fishing trips.

ENTERPRISE OF ST AGNES	1986	-	11.6m	64p	
SPIRIT OF ST AGNES	1994	-	13.4m	80p	catamaran

ENTERPRISE OF ST AGNES Formerly ran at St Martin's from 1993 to 2007 as ENTERPRISE.
SPIRIT OF ST AGNES is the only multi-hulled vessel operating in the Isles of Scilly. She was built at the Souter Shipyard, Cowes.

Spirit of St Agnes at St Mary's (Ian Boyle)

Further Reading

TRIP OUT GUIDES, Geoffrey Hamer, PO Box 485, Southall, UB1 9BH. A series of guides, regularly updated, listing the passenger boats and ferries of the UK and Europe.

FERRIES 2010, Nick Widdows, Ferry Publications (2009)

SOUTH DEVON STEAMERS & FERRIES, Alan Kittridge, Tempus (2003)

PASSENGER STEAMERS OF THE RIVER DART, Richard Clammer & Alan Kittridge, Twelveheads (1987)

PASSENGER STEAMERS OF THE RIVER FAL, Alan Kittridge – Twelveheads (1988)

PASSENGER STEAMERS OF THE RIVER TAMAR, Alan Kittridge – Twelveheads (1984)

STEAMERS & FERRIES OF CORNWALL, Alan Kittridge, Tempus (2004)

STEAMERS & FERRIES OF THE RIVER TAMAR, Alan Kittridge, Twelveheads (2003)

WEST COUNTRY PASSENGER STEAMERS, Grahame Farr, Stephenson (1967)

Index of Boats in Service 2010